WITHDRAWN FROM
THE LIBRARY
UNIVERSITY OF
WINCHESTER

D0236363

BRAVE NEW VICTUALS

AN INQUIRY INTO MODERN
FOOD PRODUCTION

By the same Author

*

THE MOTTLED LIZARD

THE FLAME TREES OF THIKA
(*Memories of an African Childhood*)

BACK STREET NEW WORLDS
A Look at Immigrants in Britain

FORKS AND HOPE

A NEW EARTH

FOUR GUINEAS
(*A Journey through West Africa*)

THE SORCERER'S APPRENTICE
(*A Journey through East Africa*)

RACE AND POLITICS IN KENYA
WITH MARGERY PERHAM

EAST AFRICA
(*Commonwealth in Pictures*)

WHITE MAN'S COUNTRY
(*Lord Delamere and the Making of Kenya*)

Novels

A MAN FROM NOWHERE

THE MERRY HIPPO

RED ROCK WILDERNESS

A THING TO LOVE

I DON'T MIND IF I DO

THE WALLED CITY

RED STRANGERS
(*A Story of Kenya*)

DEATH OF AN ARYAN

MURDER ON SAFARI

MURDER AT GOVERNMENT HOUSE

Brave New Victuals

AN INQUIRY INTO MODERN
FOOD PRODUCTION

By

ELSPETH HUXLEY

With a Foreword by
PETER SCOTT

1965

CHATTO & WINDUS
LONDON

Published by
Chatto and Windus Ltd
42 William IV Street
London W.C.2

✱

Clarke, Irwin & Co Ltd
Toronto

KING ALFRED'S COLLEGE
WINCHESTER

641.1	b6520708
63608 HUX	43938

© Elspeth Huxley, 1965
Foreword © Peter Scott, 1965
Printed in Great Britain by
T. & A. Constable Ltd
Edinburgh

'I believe that where the love of God is verily perfected, and the true spirit of government watchfully attended to, a tenderness toward all creatures made subject to us will be experienced, and a care felt in us that we do not lessen that sweetness of life in the animal creation which the Great Creator intends for them under our government.'

JOHN WOOLMAN, 1772

Quoted in the *Book of Christian Discipline of the Society of Friends*.

                      'Nor are the dead unchangeable;
Death's solid splendours life devours throughout the
   soil's lust
   The seed takes, and the thirsty roots thrust—
      And as a cabbage, kings re-enter Rome.

If the wheel did not revolve and all life upon this earth
Died in death and did not quicken,
Nor re-awaken, and the severed lay forever broken,
Then in time all life would lie absorbed in greedy
   death
And no birth from the tomb could quicken
Nor from the womb awaken. From life our death is
   taken,
From death our life is drawn.'

   RONALD DUNCAN: *This Way to the Tomb*

Contents

Author's Note

The theme touched on in these pages is one that arouses passion. People who care at all care deeply about the growing use of synthetic chemicals in our husbandry, holding these compounds either to be tools of the devil, or weapons of enlightenment; either slow poisons that will rot us all, or splendid scientific advances that will help us to overcome the hunger threatening the human race. People care no less deeply about the treatment of animals. Some believe that, by keeping them intensively, we are subjecting them to intolerable cruelties and abuses; others, that in believing this we are giving way to a sentimental emotionalism which will lead to more cruelty, not less, because animals, like humans, if properly looked after, will be better off indoors than out in all weathers, and because more humans will go hungry if we do not, by these and other methods, do our utmost to produce more food.

These views are held with deep sincerity and there is a great deal to be said on both sides.

I have attempted, I do not know with what success, to put both points of view. Naturally, this annoys everyone who takes these questions seriously; no one is more irritating than the sitter on the fence. Aristides, I believe, was stoned to death by the Athenians for that very offence. So I shall be lucky to get off with a few brickbats. But I saw no way to avoid the middle road. The scientists, with minds trained to be factual, logical and objective, have the most forcible arguments. I found few to be complacent, though some are naturally committed to a point of view. Others are uneasy; all admit the need for a

9

great deal more investigation and experiment. Biologists know well how small is the field of human certainty in any matter touching living things. But most of them consider that opponents of the use of chemicals, and of the development of intensive livestock production, have at times over-stated their case, and made assertions based on emotion rather than on logic.

But then, why should we not, in part at least, base our actions on emotion? We have this curious British puritan, rationalist fear of sentiment. Love, hate, pity, rage, tenderness and remorse do not seem to us to be respectable; if we feel such emotions, they must be concealed; like a tendency to drink too much, or bad breath, they are mildly shameful. Other ages, other nations, have not felt the same.

It would be foolish, obviously, to allow ourselves to be carried by our emotions beyond the borders of reason into the land of crackpots, cranks and the lunatic fringe. The subjects I have dealt with reach up towards the clouds of morals and ethics on the one hand, and down towards the bedrock (if it is that) of scientific fact on the other. Both need to be taken into account. Must not guesswork always play a large part in the conduct of our affairs? So the organic farmers, to whom the Soil Association acts as an umbrella, and those emotionalists angered by the caging of animals, ought not to be dismissed as harbourers of bees in bonnets, even if it is true that they ascribe to animals certain human feelings which animals very probably do not have.

About the only thing everyone agrees on is the need for more research, and the need to give a clearer pattern and direction to such research as is already in train. There is also, surely, a need for a more informed public opinion, and it is in the hope of contributing a little towards this that I have expanded and reshaped an original series of *Punch* articles into an introduction to a very big theme, or series of themes. How we humans are to combine the doubling of our numbers in the next thirty years with keeping ourselves fed, and not only fed but housed, educated, medicated and provided with an outlet for our energies and scope for recreation, while automation takes over most of the work that has formerly occupied us, is the major question of our age. (Apart from the question of whether we shall, in one sense, solve everything by blowing each other up.) So perhaps I may hope that readers will not expect tidy "solutions", nor condemn the writer for not providing them. The first stage is surely to try to weigh up the facts, in so far as anyone knows them, and in so far as anyone can.

Once more I am indebted to Mr Bernard Hollowood, the editor of *Punch*, for commissioning the original articles, and for his permission to reprint them in a revised and expanded form. A great many people have helped me to collect, arrange and check the material. Except collectively, I cannot thank them all. But I would like especially to record my gratitude to Professor A. N. Duckham, C.B.E., of Reading University, and to Mr Alexander Hay of the Association of Agriculture, for reading the typescript—without, of course, in either case, accepting any responsibility for the interpretation of the facts and speculations I have attempted to outline.

Practice and theory, farmers and scientists—I have tried to draw threads from warp and woof alike. On the farming side, I am very grateful for the help of such expert practitioners as Messrs. Jack Eastwood, Geoffrey Sykes, Tristram Beresford, David Taylor, John Byron, Sam Mayall and Wilfrid Cave, to name only a few. Among the advisers and scientists, I record with gratitude the interest and counsel of Dr Rudd Jones of the Agricultural Research Council; Mr Emrys Jones of the National Agricultural Advisory Service; Dr William Berry of the Ministry of Health; and Miss D. F. Hollingsworth of the M.A.F.F. Among scientific authorities in the commercial world I am particularly indebted to Dr W. P. Blount, director of the Poultry Advisory Service of the British Oil and Cake Mills; Dr E. F. Edson, head of Fisons' research station at Chesterford Park; Mr Stephen Williams of Boots' experimental farms in Nottinghamshire; Dr Tj. Bakker of Messrs Christopher Hill, and Dr W. R. Boon and Dr S. H. Crowdy of Imperial Chemical Industry's research station at Jealott's Hill.

Also I would like to thank those authorities at various universities and research stations who have taken so much trouble to reply with patience and care to my enquiries. It would be impossible to name them all, and to single out a few is always difficult. But I would like to say a special word of thanks to Sir Joseph Hutchinson, F.R.S., Professor of Agriculture at Cambridge, and to his colleague Dr W. H. Thorpe, F.R.S., the authority on animal behaviour. And to Dr Kenneth Mellanby, C.B.E., director of the research station of the Nature Conservancy at Monks' Wood in Huntingdonshire, who took an infinity of trouble, as did members of his staff, such as Dr Norman Moore, Dr Davis, Dr Ian Prestt and Dr Ovington; not to mention the Conservancy's deputy director, Dr Barton Worthington. Also to Dr A. N. Worden of the nearby Huntingdon Research Centre; Mr R. A. Wright, M.R.C.V.S., of the Houghton Poultry Research Station, and, further afield, Dr P. T. Thomas of the Plant Breeding Station at Aberystwyth. Also Dr Reginald Milton, scientific adviser to the Soil Association; Mr N. W. Pirie, F.R.S., of Rothamsted; Mr Syd Fox of Reading; Professor John Yudkin of the Queen Elizabeth College, Dr Paul Leyhausen of the Max-Planck-Institut für Verhaltensphysiologie at Wuppertal-Eberfeld; and many others. And to Mrs Warburton, who makes sense on the typewriter out of illegible scrawls.

Foreword by Peter Scott

In a world where two thirds of the human population are still hungry and vast numbers still die of starvation or diseases of malnutrition, a visitor from outer space would have difficulty in understanding why a large proportion of the remaining third suffers in various ways from over-eating. The same visitor would have difficulty in understanding how a species that is fully conversant with the principles of population dynamics is unable to apply that knowledge to its own survival and prosperity.

The curve of human population rises steeply, so too does the curve of food supply, but not steeply enough. Far from the gap between them closing, it continues to widen. Demand exceeds supply by more each year, not less. In increasing food production we are not even keeping up with the increasing population. The long-term answer must lie in the power of mankind to control his destiny by controlling his population—a forlorn hope, many people think, but as a practising optimist I disagree. As an animal, man is more destructive than any other, but he is also more imaginative and creative and ingenious than any other—and he has evolved a conscience. Throughout his history he has been surprisingly good at removing obstacles, at eliminating things that were clearly disadvantageous. As soon as over-population becomes clearly and *universally* disadvantageous, the problem that now looks so insoluble will be solved.

Meanwhile, back on the ranch . . . . food production must somehow be stepped up to tide over the period before man discovers that quality in life is a better aim than quantity, that fewer people with higher standards of life are better than more with lower standards. If the lesson is not learned, human beings will soon be living in much the same conditions as factory-farmed animals.

But though I am certain the lesson will eventually be learned, we have still got to step up food production, and this is where Mrs Huxley's book comes in. It looks with acute perception into the future and it deals in remarkable detail with the present trends that have caused so much concern to many, myself among them. It deals also with the reasons for that concern. Time snaps at our heels. There is no time to lose, we realise; no time for long years of research which may yield results that may be unexpected and even contradict some of our accepted beliefs. As the human flood spreads over the countryside, robbing the farmer and stockman of land needed for his crops and livestock to cover it with habitations, roads, schools, factories recreation grounds and power stations, so we must step up output from the land which remains. So we turn to those intensive forms of food production many of us instinctively dislike—battery hens, barley beef, indoor veal, sweat-box pigs and so on. We cannot afford to sit back and let the pests, weeds and diseases, formerly kept in check by traditional methods of husbandry, take a mounting toll as the opportunities offered them by modern concentrated methods of production expand. So we rush into the indiscriminate use of pesticides which kill not only the pests, but all the other insects and the creatures which feed on them; and the other creatures which in turn feed on *them*, until the food chain brings the poisons to us—not, as we are constantly assured, in harmful quantities, but in measurable amounts. To steepen that food production curve these risks may have to be taken, even though research on side effects is incomplete. If the effects of pesticides on predatory birds are a true indication, then we may reach a point where man (the most predatory of all predatory animals) begins to suffer from a similar sterility. From an overpopulation point of view it could be argued that such an accidental side effect would be quite beneficial. But if man's fecundity is to be limited surely it should not be left to a blind miscalculation which at the same time kills or sterilises so many other creatures. Surely man will demand more control of his destiny than this.

The technology of our world accelerates as "progress" rushes onwards. Only the mind of man and the speed at which it can be changed or modified or moulded to new ideas remain sadly the same, or almost the same, as ever. The adaptability of the human animal progresses inexorably at the speed of evolution by natural selection, which now includes the special social selection operated by man himself. It may take one tenth of the time that it took ten years ago to develop an electronic invention, but it still takes just as long as ever to adjust the human mind to a wholly new idea. So technology outstrips our capacity to control it and use it for the enrichment of human life. Instead, we are in danger of being used by it, and driven over the precipice like Gadarene swine in the grip of a spirit we do not understand.

Moses took the children of Israel into the wilderness for forty years. Evolution might have brought that figure down to thirty-nine years, some four thousand years later. But now we can neither afford to think in terms of thousands of years, nor even of forty. The dangers are immediate, as the gap between the under- and the over-fed widens, and through the spread of education the underfed and overcrowded come to realise that their condition is not due to the will of God or the decrees of fate, but rather to the inability of man to control his own destiny and organise his own resources. Then they will demand changes, not in forty years, but here and now.

This is the background to Mrs Huxley's inquiry. Hers is a very important book. It is about the survival of the human race, and it deals realistically not only with facts and figures, but also with human emotions—a part of the equation which planners often forget. We all like to think we are logical and rational, and motivated by what is scientifically sensible—but we all in varying degree have emotions, and bees in our bonnets too, stemming from our personal dispositions and experiences; without them we should be incomplete human beings and our decisions would be out of balance.

We are perpetually being faced with decisions—the "don't knows" are usually the smallest category in any popular poll—even though there may seem to be little enough chance of influencing the course of events by the stand we make. At least we should be informed. That is the service offered to us by this book. Elspeth Huxley has given us the facts, as she set out to do. The judgements are up to us to make.

Slimbridge,
June, 1965

Hungry Sheep

NUMBERS, that is the starting point. Sheer weight of numbers. Every second of every day, two more mouths enter the world demanding to be fed. We ought to have it all by heart now. By the year 2000, less than half an average lifetime away, there will be well over twice as many people on this man-packed planet as there are today—at least 7,000 millions, that is to say. This year, another 65 million humans will be spawned, which is equivalent to adding the population of Greater Brighton to the world every *day*, or two new Manchesters a week. In 1970, at least 72 more millions will be added, about 200,000 daily, or a new Paris every fortnight; in the year 2000 another 155 millions will appear, which is getting on for half a million daily, and would add the equivalent of nearly twenty new Londons (as it is at present) to the human score.

To match this increase, and achieve a very modest improvement in the living standards of the most acutely under-nourished, we need to *treble* our output of food. And if we look at how this population is distributed, things are even bleaker; seventy-two out of every hundred of us live in the so-called under-developed countries, and produce only forty-two per cent of the world's food. So most people—if not the local politicians—are permanently under-nourished, many downright hungry; and the rate of population increase is very much higher than it is in richer lands.

Merely to keep pace with their own natural increase, like the Red Queen running to keep in the same square, these pullulating peasants would have to produce *four* times as much food, and six times as much meat, as they do now. (Yields of meat and milk are five times higher in developed than in under-developed lands.) Impossible, of course; the gap between Western Europe, North America and Australasia, where technology steams ahead, and the rest of the world where it does not, widens year by year. So we have got to grow a lot more food or perish, unless we reduce our numbers to a manageable level by blowing ourselves up; and we cannot afford to be too fussy about how it is grown.

Ever since, in the remote dawn of human evolution, man—or, much more likely, woman—first discovered that you could plant the seeds of grasses and then reap and eat the crop, and tame wild cattle and moufflons (primitive sheep) and eat their flesh or drink their milk, there has been a close-knit partnership between man, beast and soil. Ultimately, everything came from the soil—plants, the beasts that ate the plants, and the men sustained by both these orders of creation. If man was the senior partner, he leant upon the other two and acknowledged his debt, calling the earth Mother and sometimes worshipping animals as gods.

To raise animals, he needed land to grow their food, and for them to walk about on, out of doors. "Three acres and a cow", a hundred acres and a flock of sheep, it was all the same—man, beast and land: a trinity. You could not be a farmer without a farm, until now. But now, it seems, you can.

That is the big break-through, in the jargon of the day: the discovery that you can discard one of the partners. You can have men and beasts, but no land. Or, at least, just enough to stand on, and that need not be—should not be—out of doors. You can bring the food to the animal, instead of allowing the animal to walk about and forage for itself, just as we have brought our own food to the table and do not go about any longer picking it off trees.

Clearly you can pack in very many more animals this way, and so in the same space grow much more food. Three acres and a cow: if the cattle and their progeny are packed indoors, shoulder to shoulder like broiler chickens, you can accommodate on your three acres not one but several hundreds—thousands, even, in the case of calves.

Not only that, the animals will grow much quicker indoors, mainly because they do not waste a lot of energy walking about and keeping warm in cold weather. All that energy goes into putting on flesh, or manufacturing eggs or milk. Instead of waiting for two, or even three or four, years for a calf to grow to beef size, the necessary weight will be attained in half the time, or less. Thirty years ago, it needed about fifteen weeks to convert fifteen pounds of food into a three-pound table chicken. Today, the same sized bird can be manufactured out of just over seven pounds of food in just over half the time.[1] Experimentally, scientists have produced a bird that will turn one pound of meal into one pound of chicken.

By means of this system, not only can we pack in far more animals to the acre than before, and turn them over twice as fast, we can double the quantity of animals that our buildings will accommodate. This should reduce our costs and overheads. So not only can we produce more food more quickly, we ought to do it more cheaply as well. Considering how many people in the world are desperately poor, this is tremendously important. To-day's supermarket chicken is a fairly low-priced food

[1] The precise figures are:

	Feed required	Time required
1930	15·0 lb	14-15 weeks
1960	7·2 lb	8-9 weeks

already, and broiler breeders claim that in a few years it will be the poor man's cheapest source of protein in Asia, Africa and the Middle East.

The food for all these animals inhabiting their sheds, boxes and pens still comes from the soil, and so the divorce between land and animal is not complete. It is only one stage removed, just as it is for humans; however city-bound, we still derive our nourishment from land or sea. A little is synthetic, but not much—yet. That may be the next, and even more momentous, break-through —the production, on a world scale, of synthetic edible matter. (A safer phrase than "food".) Chemicals cunningly flavoured and processed from the naked elements or from industrial by-products without the intervention of soil, husbandry, crop or creature. Then the divorce of man from his environment will be complete and irreversible. The land will serve us only as a source of minerals, a spectacle perhaps, certainly a recreation ground; a foundation for our buildings, roads and airfields—an adjunct, rather than an element of being; not a partner, but a slave.

Whether or not we *like* all this is irrelevant. We are at the mercy of our own fecundity. And technology is a juggernaut; you cannot halt it except by blowing it up. Many of us do not like it at all, but are reduced to making a few personal gestures as ineffective as they are spasmodic: buying wholemeal, stone-ground, compost-nourished flour; stopping at farms to buy free-range eggs, which often are not free-range-produced at all, at twice their normal price; refusing packaged meat at supermarkets. Like so many battery hens, we are caught up in the process, caged in our economy, trapped by trends we do not seem able to control, reverse or avoid.

All this, people often say, is "against nature". But what does that mean? Evolution is a continuous process

22

in the course of which man has gradually gained control over his fellow-species, and over his general environment. Where does he stop? Why stop at all? His precursors swung themselves about in branches. Ought man to have stayed there, instead of coming down to walk upright? (A lot of digestive disorders have arisen from this change of posture, man's insides having been slung from the spine; now the spine is vertical instead of horizontal, his insides sag; we would almost certainly have fewer ulcers if we went about on all fours, since it is against nature to stand upright.)

Then humans took to living bunched together in settlements which became towns. Most unnatural, that. Came the industrial revolution: megalopolis, conurbations, subtopia; mass production, mechanisation, the triumph of materialism, the death of craftmanship. Now we stand on the threshold of the new, computer revolution, threatened by rule by the machines, by an abdication of human judgement. If this is really so, where did we go off the rails? How do nuclear power stations, automated factories or space-probing capsules differ in their fundamentals from the pump, the windmill or the muzzle-loader, all dangerous innovations once—against nature? Should we have gone on hauling water in leather buckets instead of inventing suction pumps and harnessing the wind with a lot of cogs and mathematics? What were men endowed with arms for if it was not to use an oar? All this rigmarole with sails and ropes and masts goes against nature; what do we need a compass for, when God gave us the stars?

Progress in technology is indivisible; to draw a line and say "here is the boundary" is impossible; no one would agree on where it should run. There is no basic difference between the discovery of gunpowder, and of nuclear fission leading to a megaton bomb. Both were technical advances, enabling man to pursue with greater efficiency the dictates of his will: in both cases, the killing of his fellow-men.

So what is happening now, why are we so uneasy? Maybe it is the speed that alarms us. Time is a dimension; time has run away; like a revved-up engine minus its governor, time is racing ahead out of harmony. A horse, a coach, a car, an aircraft—all perfectly all right so long as their speed remains under control. A bolting horse, a runaway coach, an over-driven car and a plummeting aircraft have one end only, total disaster. Is that the end to which we fear all this accelerated progress in technology, this social change, may lead us?

This preamble really states one of our conclusions: that the full and long-delayed impact of the industrial revolution on our countryside is on the way and cannot be stopped, any more than we could stop the pump, the windmill or the muzzle-loader in their day. We are firmly planted on the escalator and we cannot turn round and run the other way.

With this proposition a lot of thoughtful, able and uneasy people do not agree. Technology, they think, *can* be halted, short of a point where it destroys our souls and, very possibly, poisons our bodies. It can, and must, be controlled. We are, after all, the masters. It is true that the one order of creation we have so far failed to master is ourselves. That does not mean we shall never do so. In the field of human combat, the need to control our own technology is so plain that no one disputes it, or at least no one in the West. Nuclear warfare could equal, more or less, human suicide. In the field of ecology, the field of balance—the balance between plants, animals and their environment; the balance between the various orders, such as man and beast, within the whole; and then the balance of one species with another, an ever-changing set of adjustments and changes—in this more complex field, the need for control is less obvious, but every bit as profound.

We can poison, starve or spiritually maim each other just as easily as kill each other outright. Of the two, the first is probably the more likely; so let us, say our modern zealots, take heed before it is too late and, by renouncing some of the benefits of modern technology, save our souls. Step off the escalator jolting to disaster, or put it into reverse.

Can this be done? Before deciding, we had better take a look at the general direction in which the escalator appears to be carrying us along.

Life Sentence

B y now we all know what they look like, even if only on a television screen: rows and rows and rows of hens thrusting red-combed necks out of tiers and tiers of cages, as an automatic feeding machine replenishes the trough into which their beaks are plunged. Thousands and thousands of prisoners, gripping on to slanted wire slats under a dim artificial light, packed in together, barely able to spread their wings or turn round; machines for manufacturing eggs. Directly their efficiency falters, off they go to slaughter, their brief, unnatural, joyless lives at an end.

The belief is widespread that this is cruel or, even if it falls short of actual cruelty, then degrading both to man and bird. Even if it is true that battery hens lay the cheapest eggs, is not there a limit to how far we should go in treating living creatures simply as machines? Is not a bird, like a human, born with some natural rights, including those of freedom to exercise its basic instincts to peck, scratch, walk about, spread its wings, select its food and even mate in due season?

The Danes have passed a law banning battery cages, and Danes are nothing if not hard-headed. But this legislation was not introduced—in 1950—mainly in the interests of the birds; it formed part of a social policy designed to support family farmers, and to stop big business moving in to squeeze out the small man.

Scientists are divided. "I wouldn't be allowed to keep my experimental birds in these conditions," a Fellow of the Royal Society said. "Under the anti-vivisection laws, a caged bird must have room to stretch its wings. These laws don't apply to poultry." Another scientist commented: "Domestic fowls don't normally fly anyway, and have been bred for generations for docility. The judgement's a subjective one." As usual, two sides.

Rather more than one-third of our eggs come from battery hens, about forty-five per cent from those in deep-litter houses, and less than one-fifth from birds on free range. The battery method is gaining ground from both the other systems. On average, it results in more eggs per bird; the official estimate is an average of 220 in battery cages, 210 on deep litter and only 180 on free range. Some of the highest flock averages are reached in deep-litter houses, but costs are higher too, because more labour is needed. Whereas the most one man can hope to deal with on deep litter is about 5,000 birds, Mr J. B. Eastwood (of whom more later) has one girl in charge of 26,000 birds in a single battery house, and time-and-motion studies have indicated that her job could be reduced to under four hours a day. It consists mainly of two things: transferring eggs to a moving belt which takes them, without further human intervention, into a packing station to be automatically candled, graded and packed; and removing dead birds.

It is true that most battery birds—many deep-litter ones too, for that matter—never see daylight. They start as day-old chicks in big sheds, warmed by infra-red lamps. Clean, fresh water and well-balanced meal is constantly before them and they eat all they want. Fans suck out their stale, moist exhalations, to be replaced by fresh air. In a house containing 10,000 adult birds, about two tons of water will be deposited daily; this must be extracted, or the litter will turn soggy and the birds die, often with blistered breasts.

Light regulates the growth and reproduction of the bird by its action on the pituitary gland, which releases a hormone which in turn stimulates the ovary. A power station does the job rather better than the sun. The chicks start in an "autumn situation"; hours of light are tapered down to eight in twenty-four. Comes artificial spring; every day the lights stay on longer, the birds respond, and by the time they are between five and six months old, and are getting about fourteen hours of daily illumination, they should be laying in their litter-houses or cages. There they stay for forty-nine to fifty-one weeks, unless they die, or look so poorly they are culled, laying for all they are worth with the season stuck at midsummer (seventeen hours light). Towards the end their artificial day shortens, and then the time arrives for their journey to the slaughter-house, more politely called a packing station. No battery birds are kept a second season. A short life, if not a gay one.

The word "light" needs a little stretching, because it has been discovered that very little light will do. Birds can be reared almost in the dark, a system known as "twilighting". This cuts power costs, and has a soothing effect on the birds. In semi-darkness, they do not quarrel, feather-peck or tear out each other's vents. (In one flock, one bird in ten had previously died of a savaged vent.) They do not need de-beaking, as they often do in stronger light, and later on convert their food more economically into eggs.

Three tiny bulbs, each only five-eighths of a watt strong, can suffice for a shed about 100 feet by 20 feet holding 2,000 birds. At first it looks as black as pitch, but once your eyes adapt themselves it is about the same as a clear, starlit night without a moon. The actual measurable intensity is one-twentieth of a foot-candle, or lumen.

Is all this cruel? Certainly it is "unnatural". But so are all forms of farming. It is unnatural for a cow to give more milk than her calf needs, unnatural for a steer to reach maturity in two years instead of five—or even to be a steer at all, not a bull; and nothing is more unnatural than fields of wheat or barley, which are really grasses tricked by plant breeders into bearing ten, twenty, perhaps a hundred times more grain than they naturally require for the simple purpose of re-seeding themselves. If domestic hens, derived from jungle fowls, had stayed natural, they would lay two annual clutches of about fifteen eggs each. Battery birds may be *more* unnatural than free-range ones, but it is a matter of degree.

All the same, are battery birds really comfortable? They live on wire floors slanted forwards to allow the eggs to roll clear. A bird's foot is designed for perching and it cannot perch on wire. The bird has to grip awkwardly and it is always at a slight angle. Perhaps it will adapt itself, to some extent, as the caged inmates of an enormous broiler rabbit unit seem to be doing by giving birth to young with thickened pads on their hind legs to cope with the wire.

In the beginning, birds were put singly into cages, then doubled up. Now they are often packed in seven, nine, even forty or fifty birds to a cage of the appropriate size. The minimum allowance is 0·6 square feet per bird, but 0·7 square feet is probably nearer the norm. That means, roughly, nine birds in a cage two feet by three. Not a lot of *Lebensraum*. As a rule, each bird gets four inches of the trough which runs along outside the mesh of "cafeteria cages", and is automatically filled. The most up-to-date batteries have drinking nozzles in each cage, from which the birds soon learn to suck. They are not all that dumb.

Certainly the birds *look* overcrowded; shoulder to shoulder, they are pressed up against each other scarcely able to move. It would be like spending your whole life in the rush-hour in the underground and this would drive *us* off our heads, so we assume they must hate it too. Our weakness is we cannot ask them, we merely burden them with our feelings. Are we right, or are we victims of a fallacy?

"Disposition to inflict suffering; indifferent to or taking pleasure in another's pain", is the Shorter Oxford Dictionary's definition of cruelty. In that case, battery cages are not cruel. They do not inflict actual pain. If they do inflict some discomfort, no one takes pleasure in it, because discomfort does not help a bird to thrive.

We do not inflict, we deprive. Is deprivation cruel? To take away, or at the least greatly to curtail, freedom to move, to choose, to breed, to develop as an individual? For each animal *is* an individual, or carries that potentiality, even if it is rudimentary. Even among shoal-dwelling fishes, it seems, there are leaders and the led. There is a boss among minnows.

Yet battery-keepers have a case. "People think it's always summer on a farm," said one rather bitterly. "They talk about discomfort in a battery cage. How about discomfort in the pelting rain in January in a yard a foot deep in icy slush, with a biting north-east wind? My battery birds are warm, dry and well fed. They are a lot better off than many a bird in a dirty, draughty, leaking old henhouse in a back yard, knee-deep in mud and fed on scraps, menaced by foxes and stoats. If a bird is unhappy—and this applies to any animal—it will show this in two ways. It will go off its feed, and fail to breed. These birds eat splendidly. Their combs are bright, they lay eggs and lay well. They have nothing to fear, and I'm satisfied they are not suffering from distress."

Those are the two tests everyone mentions: a contented bird eats and thrives and, if it lives long enough, breeds normally, or at least shows willing, i.e. lays eggs. The obverse is certainly true: an animal that is really miserable will not eat, and will not breed.

Is that the whole story? Eating, first. Humans in prisons often put on weight. That is a matter of diet, not contentment. Also it is a fact that sufferers from long-enduring and severe grief often decline into obesity, not because grief in itself is fattening, but because they lose interest in normal activities and so do not use up their store of chemical energy. (Queen Victoria grew immensely fat after the death of her Consort.) Battery hens cannot move about to use up energy, so put it all into flesh and eggs. As for laying, they are prisoners of heredity. Human ingenuity has so combined their genes that they must lay until they die, or reach the final stages of some incurable disease. Even an epidemic of fowl pest, an infection of the breathing apparatus, may cause only a minor set-back: in one case a falling off, on average, of only two eggs per bird.

There is a general lay belief that free-range birds are healthier than those kept in cages or on deep litter. This does not appear to be so. In so far as figures are available, they suggest that battery birds have the lowest mortality and lay the best eggs. Quality, judged by such factors as thin versus sturdy shells, discoloured yolks and "watery whites", can be a measure of non-lethal disease. In Lancashire, still primarily a land of small flocks and backyard birds kept in crowded and insanitary conditions, twice as many eggs are down-graded by the packing stations as is the case elsewhere. By contrast, well-managed deep-litter flocks are kept relatively free from the bacteria and viruses which cause disease.

If things go wrong, of course they can go very wrong indeed. Instead of losing half a dozen birds you may lose hundreds, thousands even. Diseases, if not checked in

time, can spread like bush-fires. By mechanising everything, hostages have been given to fortune on a frighten-
ing scale. Today it is no longer the farmer and the stockman who really matter, it is the accountant and the
engineer. If the ventilation packs up, in a few hours the
birds die. The man in the power-house holds in his hands
the life of the bird in its cage.

In a battery house in which I listened to the birds
crooning as they thrust alert, beady-eyed faces and
snowy necks through the wire, my companion, a lec-
turer in animal husbandry, spoke of the researches of Dr
Erich Baeumer of Germany, author of *Das dumme Huhn*,
into the "language" of fowls. This Dr Baeumer has
analysed into thirty-five basic "sentences", or patterns
of sound, each of which conveys a message. There is a
different signal for danger that threatens from the
ground or from the air, and sounds to express such
feelings as alarm, curiosity, anger, satisfaction, recog-
nition, pain and pride.

"Hens vary a lot as individuals," said my companion.
"Some are talkative, some reserved; they use a universal
language; they understand each other, from all over the
world. Love and sex are not important; food and danger
are. The sound they are making now is curiosity. When
the trough is filled it is satisfaction. They 'talk' most of
the day." Outwardly, they seemed quite contented. A
few weeks later, a lot of them were dead—suffocated in
their cages as a result of an unheralded power cut.

Possibly the relative good health of battery and deep-
litter birds is due to their youth. They are killed before
they have had time to do much ailing, except for fowl
paralysis (*leucosis*) which often strikes the young. A
batch of experimental birds maintained under intensive
conditions by Dr Alan Greenwood of Edinburgh, who
has kept fowls this way for over thirty years, remained as

sent prices plummeting, and sor
from potential agribusinessmen. T
gobbled up the most of the small
1,000 growers produce ninety per
marketed, and three giants have t

The breeding side is narrowec
inevitably, because it is very costl;
powered geneticists must be emp
States, five breeders select almost a
and six the broilers, all 2,000 mil
following along the same lines.
3,000 breeders supplied the hatcl
old chicks to poultry farmers; toda
to twelve; tomorrow there will be

While this delights agribusines
more doubtful. "Our big probl
diseases are transmitted in the egg
our breeding stock gets infected?
hit literally millions of birds ove
We know too little about how these
to take such a gamble." This has
the last ten years leukaemia, unkno
been introduced, through breec
Indian sub-continent. Geneticists
to discard so many possible genet
our fertile eggs in half a dozen ba
are the bank on which you draw i
characteristic in your bird. To give
pecking used to be a major probl
bred most of the aggression out o
though not out of those—more higl
for laying. If the genes carrying a h
had been discarded, this might hav

Growers started with broiler nu
miniscule, a few thousands; to

a tender, small, oven-ready, quick-to-cook, uniform and
clean bird. In ten years they have turned poultry meat
from a luxury into fodder for the masses, and all without
any help from the taxpayer, who subsidises beef and
mutton by nearly eightpence a pound.

Agribusiness is the whole business of producing and
marketing food, not just growing it on farms. It has three
main branches: supplying things to the farmer (tractors,
fuel, machinery, seeds, sprays, fertilisers and so on); the
actual farming; and getting the products on to the consumer's plate (processing, storing, transport, packaging
and distribution). The importance of the middle stage,
the actual growing of the food, has been waning, while
the before and after stages have waxed. Fifty years ago
the American farmer's slice of the whole cheese was
fifty-four per cent, today it is down to seventeen per cent
and still dwindling; for every man working on the land,
two are employed on off-the-farm activities. Although in
Britain we spend less than the Americans on processing,
packaging and distributing our food, Mr Sykes estimates
£75 out of every £100 worth of agribusiness to be spent
off, not on, the farm. The trend continues.

While most people view with alarm or, at the least,
regret, this continuing exodus from the land, Mr Sykes
thinks it ought to go faster and farther. Our farmlands
are split into about 345,000 holdings, still far too many
in his view, and we have nearly one million men, all told,
on the land. At least half of these, he considers, should
soon repair to cities, to clear the way for more specialisa-
tion, bigger and fewer units, greater capital investment,
higher output per man, slide-rule and push-button
techniques and fierce competition—the rats to be raced
not only through the urban corridors of power but round
the rural air-conditioned barn and pathogen-free cowshed. Let us, he suggests, welcome rather than deplore

these changes; save the
year in subsidies, and ge

All our broiler stocks
They are a creation of ge
genes to produce a bird sc
for slaughter, at an avera
and a half to ten weeks a
and so economical at co
can turn two and a half p
one pound of chicken. Al
not have done because th
the stocks from which the
the techniques evolved fr
hybrid maize, which in t
national yield, and resul
her livestock production

The British broiler
smuggling. Right dowr
poultry breeding stock
officially on account of dis
and repute would return
anxiously nursing illicit
continental holidays load
scent stowed away in the b
Awkward things to smug
were eased with the adve
flying time from Boston
hours, and enabled peri
from American roosters t
margin of about half an

So broilers started, a
attracted people whose
whose bank balances we
aheaders with peeled ey
ground. After the honey

economic unit is probably 50,000 birds reared and cleared four times a year, an annual output of at least 200,000. The next objective is to lop about a week off the growing period so as to fit in five batches of chicks in a year. This, if achieved, will lower costs by spreading overheads and capital, and bring about an even cheaper broiler. Already growers operate on a margin of about a penny a pound.

This does not mean that only big firms with enormous capital resources, or tycoons like Messrs Ross, Buxteds and Eastwood, will stay in the business. The broiler-grower may become, increasingly, a contractor working for a large firm. The firm will own the following: mills to grind and mix meal; a transport fleet to deliver it; a chain of slaughter-houses; teams and lorries to catch and collect the birds and clear out the deep litter; hatcheries geared to feed the right numbers of chicks into the broiler houses, every week, all the year round; a central rearing unit to supply the cocks and pullets that produce fertile eggs that will hatch into day-old broiler chicks. This is called vertical integration.

There is no end to the other things a vertically integrated broiler firm may own, such as factories to treat the offal—guts, feathers, heads and claws get processed, ground up and returned to the broiler's food as a source of protein—and construction businesses to make the sheds and their equipment. Then there is the selling side. A few mammoth firms, eight or at most a dozen, are mopping up the surviving small retailers. The independent grocer is already up against it, and now butchers and fishmongers and poulterers are feeling the crunch. The big chains will probably tie up, if they have not already done so, with agribusiness, thereby cutting costs, increasing efficiency, stream-lining it all; and we will get cheaper, cleaner, tenderer, handsomer food in neater packages, more pleasing to the eye.

The price we will pay for all this? Personal service, the fun of picking things out, the differences, the *interest* of shopping; and, as many think, a good deal of the food's quality and flavour. So also goes a lot of waste, staleness and germs, along with flavour and freshness. We should all like to have our cake and eat it. You cannot sell a blemished apple in the supermarket, but you *can* sell a tasteless one, provided it is shiny, smooth, even, uniform and bright. And so the grower has to spray and spray against orchard pests, up to fourteen times. But—murderous things, these chemical sprays (grumble the consumers), loading us with devilish poisons; we want no sprays, but also no blemishes—all this, and heaven too.

"Vertical integration," Mr Geoffrey Sykes has written, "is changing the role of farmers by shifting to others their responsibilities as managers." So in future—if he is right—it will no longer be for Farmer Giles to decide what to grow, or even how to grow it; that decision will lie with Mrs Jones in the supermarket. Canadian broilermen decided, or rather their computers did, that a four-pound bird was the most economical to produce. But Mrs Canadian Jones found that, when split in two, it did not fit into her television dinner-tray, so now the growers are marketing a two-and-a-half-pound "junior broiler". As for farmers, "they must learn to give business analysis priority over the practical work on the farm" and perform the task allotted them by agri-businessmen with slide-rule and computer, instead of tractor and fork. Mr Antony Fisher, a broiler baron, has summarised the position. "The consumer comes first. If you try to put the producer before the consumer, it becomes necessary to resist change. Progress means change and we all want progress. The object of production must be consumption. Contract farming is one way

41

of trying to ensure that only that which is required is produced. Instead of many minds making many judgements in the chain of production, the single judgement by one company can be more orderly. We cannot, in the future, put up with haphazard production of food by farmers." Farmers indeed! Agribusinessmen with their computers will do it all very much better.

Most of the farmers will work part-time in industry. "Production per worker is going to go up fourfold, six-fold, sometimes tenfold," Mr Sykes has prophesied. "Instead of one man to 20 cows, one man to 100; instead of one man to 1,000 layers, one to 10,000." In California, it is nothing out of the way for one man to attend to up to 30,000 layers dropping 25,000 eggs a day, an investment of £50,000 per poultryman employed. Farmer Giles, taking a stroll with a gun under his arm, leaning on gates and talking about mangelwurzels, or even about power take-offs and chemical sprays, is just about as 'with it' as a muzzle-loader in the Pentagon, or a dog-cart on the M1.

Son George, a contractor-specialist in broilers, supplied by agribusiness with the chicks, their food and litter, with fuel, medicines, supervision, transport, advice and a team to clear his sheds between each batch of chicks, will himself contribute the houses and their equipment, the skill and labour, and that is about all. He will get paid so much a bird. Most responsibilities and worries he will have shed. Markets and prices are not his affair. He will be a technician rather than a farmer. Of course there will still be good technicians and bad; some will make profits and some will not; but, either way, son George can look forward to more leisure, less sweat, much less responsibility, better pay and, possibly, less interest out of life than his father. That is the way it goes. I was talking the other day to a smallholder who has not had a full day off for twenty-three years. He, himself, does not regret it, but none of his children will ever milk a cow or feed a hen.

A broilerman I visited employed one girl to look after his three houses, each containing 10,000 birds, and about all she had to do, he said, was to walk round each house twice a day, which took half an hour in the morning and another in the afternoon, to remove the dead or dying. "In theory, you could leave the birds for the whole of their ten-week growing period without going near them." For everything is automatic—food, water, light. The meal goes round in something called a Big Dutchman which, launched by a time-switch, hourly conveys the food round miles of trough, on a chain. The house is windowless; day and night, ventilator fans whir, sucking and expelling air in calculated quantities. The lighting, too, is automatic; all round the clock it alternates between a rest period of an hour and a half, when it is muted and faintly rosy, and then half an hour for feeding and walking about, when it is comparatively bright.

The birds are packed in tight: 0·7 or 0·8 of a square foot per bird is the normal allowance, that is when they are nearly ready to go for slaughter. Are they over-crowded, and if so does this matter? The poultry experts say no. On the other hand, a broilerman told me that when one-third of a batch of 10,000 chicks was wiped out by an epidemic, the survivors grew so much faster that they averaged four pounds instead of three and a half when ready for slaughter, and almost made up in total weight for the dead birds.

Broilers, unlike battery hens, can move about; they are gregarious creatures, and most chicks are normally reared indoors. There seems to be no active cruelty here; just mass production, automatic and mechanised, of

43

rather dull food for masses of humans, most of whom live mechanised and rather dull lives.

Soon after this, I went to Gatwick airport on a Bank Holiday. In a huge building, artificially lit, thousands and thousands of humans were milling about, shoulder to shoulder, or sitting on benches clutching bags; from them came a constant half muttering, half chirping sound; no one was hurrying anywhere in particular, but very few were still. They seemed vaguely to be waiting or looking for something—the Big Dutchman, rolling silently by? Now and then a uniformed attendant moved purposefully about, keeping an eye on the inmates. I did not see any feather-pecking. And everyone seemed happy enough—warm, dry and well fed.

Testing

IF you pack into one place large numbers of living things, whether broilers or calves, people or tomato plants, it stands to reason that epidemics and diseases will become intensified. Poultry are disease-prone at the best of times, and now that indoor techniques are spreading, so are losses caused by the various bacteria and viruses which prey on them.

There are at least nine major poultry diseases.[1] While actual deaths in rearing are thought to average about seven chicks out of every hundred, this suggests a sub-clinical morbidity of something like forty per cent: that is, forty birds out of every hundred have some degree of infection, though not one that kills them outright. In other words, a lot of poultry go for slaughter before they have an opportunity to die. Others, of course, would in time recover from their degree of non-acute infection.

Researchers are busy seeking remedies and vaccines to protect the birds, and they have had some notable successes. Coccidiosis used to be one of the worst killers, and now it is under control—thanks to the use of modern antibiotics.

The situation has its dangers, however. The pathogens which cause diseases are being suppressed rather than eliminated. "Probably ninety-nine per cent of the birds in most of our flocks carry some degree of coccidiosis infection," I was told at a poultry research station. "Five different bacilli are involved, each one of which

[1] These are: fowl pox, epidemic tremor, infectious bronchitis, laryngo-tracheitis, Newcastle disease, myooptaema gallisepticum, infectious synovitis, lymphomatosis and fowl paralysis.

reacts differently to drugs. Most of the birds' natural resistance has been done away with, and they depend almost wholly on antibiotics. If it were not for these, coccidiosis would rampage."

Every animal's digestive system is the home of count-less millions of streptococci, bacteria, viruses and other organisms collectively known as the micro-flora, and comprising innumerable species. Upon these, anti-biotics exercise a profound and, as yet, little known effect: suppressing some, encouraging others and changing the balance. Since most of these micro-organisms seem to be parasitic on the animal, antibiotics exercise, on the whole, a beneficial effect, enabling them to put on weight more thriftily and to keep in better health.

But, as in many other cases, farm practice has forged ahead of scientific knowledge. We know that small quantities of antibiotics, when added to their rations, will speed up the growth of calves, piglets, chicks and other young creatures. Batches of calves, for instance, have put on as much as one-third more weight in the same time as batches which have not been given anti-biotics, and fewer have died from complaints such as bloat. In some large-scale experiments carried out by the Agricultural Research Council, the addition of penicillin or aureomycin to the rations of fattening pigs increased their live-weight gain, on average, by ten to fourteen per cent—in individual cases, by up to forty per cent; and their food conversion efficiency improved by six to seven per cent. We know this happens, but we do not know why in any detail: we do not know which antibiotics (there are dozens) affect which kinds of micro-organism (there are thousands); even more important, we do not know how lasting these effects will be.

The natural state of all living creatures is a constant

struggle for survival, and micro-organisms are particularly good at hitting back. A fantastic rate of reproduction is their main defence. By dividing itself every twenty minutes, a single organism may give rise to about a million offspring in about twelve hours.

Among the unimaginably large and varied micro-flora to be found in the guts of any animal, some strains will display an ability to overcome a new synthetic drug. How or why this should be so is a profound mystery. But so it is: and this property can be inherited. Thus will arise, often with startling speed, strains of bacteria, viruses and streptococci resistant to the drugs which kill the majority. So next time there is an epidemic, your penicillin, aureomycin, chlortetracylin, or whatever, will fail to do its job. This has already happened and is happening now. In hospitals, strains of staphylococci which resist the antibiotic streptomycin, used to treat the infection, have emerged within two or three days.

Biochemists counter-attack in several directions. They keep on discovering new antibiotics which will knock out the new resistant strains. But, in the words of Dr R. Scarisbrick of the Agricultural Research Council, "bacteria can cope with new antibiotics faster than these can be discovered, and we should not assume that the process of discovery can go on indefinitely". Another method is continually to ring the changes between one antibiotic and another, in the hope that if one of them does not defeat the resistant strain, another will. Up to a point, this works; but scientists simply do not know enough about the whole subject, which is immensely complex, to proscribe with any certainty foolproof methods of dealing with resistant strains.

Fortunately, perhaps, antibiotics are expensive and this, plus an element of caution, restricts the quantities put into feedingstuffs. Manufacturers of chick feeds, for

instance, have agreed to confine the range to three—
procaine penicillin, aureomycin and terramycin—and to
limit the quantity to 100 grams a ton. In practice, few
manufacturers add more than ten grams because of the
cost, and because it is doubtful whether higher dosages
have a corresponding effect. Ten grams of procaine
penicillin, aureomycin or terramycin to a ton of meal,
they say, is much too small a quantity to affect a human
weighing forty or fifty times as much as a broiler; in any
case, cooking destroys most of the drug.

Other doubts arise. The animals who benefit most
from antibiotics in their rations tend to be those which,
were they humans, would be known as under-privileged
—runt pigs, the least productive laying hens, unthrifty
calves. By stepping up their productivity with drugs, we
could mask inherent weaknesses and perpetuate our least
efficient strains. Suppose we bred from these, should we
bring into use inferior genetic stocks which would otherwise disappear by the process of natural selection? Some
say yes, but some say no because there is no proof that a
runt pig, say, is *genetically* inferior to its litter-mates; its
size and scruffiness may be due merely to its accidental
assignment at the milk-bar to a stingier teat. Similarly, a
hen may be unthrifty not because her genes have so
ordained, but because of an inferior position in the peck
order. Such questions abound, and we respond not with
answers but with guesses and opinions; the need for
more research, systematic and sustained, is pressing.

Then there is the question of mastitis. This infection
of the cow's udder is widespread in our dairy herds. It is
treated by squeezing little tubes of penicillin or aureomycin up the cow's teats. If you then milk the cow, some
of the drug naturally gets into the milk. A recent survey
of 40,000 samples of milk showed that eleven per cent
contained penicillin and about one per cent other anti-

biotics. A rule made by the Milk Marketing Board forbids farmers to send away milk from cows treated for mastitis within forty-eight hours of the treatment. This is the sort of rule that cannot be enforced without an army of inspectors, in fact one in almost every cowshed in the land.

The danger is not only that people, as well as animals, may acquire immunity to the effects of antibiotics, but that people who are allergic to penicillin will suffer discomfort, and have their sensitivity to the drug increased. And there is another risk, though perhaps a rare one: that certain antibiotics may do actual bodily harm. One called chloramphenicol, sometimes used in the treatment of mastitis, can fatally disorganise the marrow of the bone. There is also some risk of trouble in cheese factories, through the slaughter by these drugs of bacteria which "work" in curd to ripen cheeses.

So there is still plenty to be found out. Plenty of scientists are trying to do so, and it is not true that, as some believe, new drugs are launched without proper tests having first been made. Anyone who thinks this should be disabused by the fact that in 1963 over four million experiments were carried out on living animals in Britain alone, one-quarter of them being "mandatory tests for the standardisation of sera, vaccines or drugs". The number of animals so used in the United States is astronomical. Several kinds of monkey are even threatened with extinction by a demand from research laboratories which has reached such a scale that a single university (Detroit) recently placed an order for 10,000 specimens from Thailand, a number estimated to exceed all the survivors in that country, after years of exports on a mounting scale.

One complication is the enormous numbers of new products that pour from the laboratories of a thriving and expanding chemical industry. Today there are said to be some 1,500 chemical additives that may be put into our food to preserve, dye or bleach it, render it more tender, palatable or nutritious, make it smell more or less, or improve its appearance; let alone what goes into our cosmetics, detergents, clothing and so on; and the number constantly rises. To test the permutations and combinations of all these would take armies of scientists, years of time and millions of pounds. About as much as can be coped with is to test each new drug on its own.

That is all right so far as it goes, but it does not go far enough, because, while chemicals A and B, used independently, may be harmless as raindrops, when mixed together in the living body may combine to form chemical X with quite different, and perhaps harmful, properties. This is known as synergism, and there have been some rather sinister examples. Recently two researchers at the University of Connecticut injected very small quantities of two common drugs, sulphanil-amide and 6-aminonicotinamide, into fertile eggs, both singly and in combination. Singly, no harm came to the embryos, which hatched normally into healthy chicks. But mixed drugs, like mixed drinks, resulted in so different a story that even scientists soberly reporting in *Nature* were persuaded to describe the contrast as "truly dramatic". After 13 days of life, 99 out of every 100 chicks hatched from eggs treated with separate doses of the drugs were strong and healthy; when the two drugs were combined, only 20 out of every 100 chicks were normal, the remaining 80 deformed. (Parrot beaks and "an extreme and crippling form" of micromelia.) "It is clear from the foregoing," pronounced the researchers, "that altogether harmless amounts of potentially terato-genic substances may in combination produce powerful synergism, and thereby a high incidence of severe mal-formations."[1]

Another major snag is that rats, mice, dogs and mon-keys have to stand in for you and me. This inability to experiment with human beings—unless you happen to be in charge of a concentration camp—constantly frustrates the conscientous scientist. The thalidomide disaster was a case in point. I visited the laboratories where the British tests were carried out. They are among the largest and most up to date in Europe, staffed by highly competent scientists and equipped with over 10,000 experimental animals. Each new drug and product is tested first on small mammals such as mice or guinea-pigs and then on larger ones like monkeys and dogs.

One of the most unnerving sights I have seen was an assembly of five hundred young dogs kept for such experiments. Beautiful pedigree spaniels and corgis. Physically, their conditions are excellent. Each dog has a clean concrete cell, ample food and drink and as much exercise as even the best of keepers can provide for five hundred young, high-spirited animals. The man in charge is a dedicated dog-lover. His predicament is haunting. "Many is the sleepless night I've had," he said. "But I've concluded that it is better for a man who cares to be in charge, than for someone who isn't a dog-lover."

There is no unnecessary suffering. If there is some-thing wrong with the drug, of course, the dog *will* suffer, possibly from cancer; but from a human angle that is not unnecessary. At the end of each experiment, every dog is killed and a post-mortem made. Had the babies been saved from thalidomide, as many humans *have* been

[1] *Nature*, 1st August, 1964. "Teratogenic Risks of Drug Synergism," Landoner and Clark.

saved from other dangerous substances by filtering these through animals, the dogs would not have died in vain.

When we entered one of the kennels, a tremendous surge of barking greeted us, with every eager prisoner crying for the one thing he could not have, a human's attention. Some would be sacrificed to ensure that teenagers did not come out in spots from a fresh shade of lipstick, or that a new hair-dye did not irritate the scalp of an old mutton trying to dress like lamb. But others would die in the interests of safety to human users of rat poisons, weed-killers, paints, pigmeals and every kind of drug and patent medicine, and also in such worthy causes as healthier diets for minks, budgerigars and sledge-dogs, the elimination of green yolks in eggs and the discovery of whether too much zinc in drinking water was to blame for constipation in a herd of cows.

Thalidomide passed these tests—not because of careless screening but mainly because animals and humans are not fully interchangeable. In the last resort, people must test drugs designed for people. Some of the ultimate effects may be gradual and cumulative. It is only in the last ten or fifteen years that the use of many crop sprays, drugs, and additives to animal feeds, based on synthetic substances hitherto unknown to mankind, has become really widespread. We are merely on the threshold of intensive methods of raising the animals on which we feed. Some of the results of our new techniques could take effect not on ourselves, but on our children, through their action on our chromosomes and genes, our genetic stock-in-trade. Some of these effects, of course, could be beneficial. Not all mutations are bad; on the contrary, biological progress has come about through the good ones.

The late President Kennedy set up a high-powered scientific committee to assess the dangers to human health of the many new chemicals, mainly the synthetic pesticides, so recently launched upon the world. Its members were not complacent. The use of these pesticides, they said, must be continued, but the risks are real and our state of knowledge inadequate. "The symptoms caused by pesticide toxicity are little different from those of many common illnesses." A British committee, set up under Sir Harold Sanders to conduct a similar review, was more bland. Its members found "no evidence of chronic effects from continued ingestion of food containing traces of pesticides"—they all use this majestic, mandarin English; and no evidence, either, "to support the suggestion that small amounts of pesticides are possibly responsible for certain human diseases which have been recognised only recently, and to which no definite causes can yet be assigned".

You cannot find evidence of anything unless you go out to look for it, and there has been all too little of that. It is an expensive game. On the other hand, you should not say, for instance, that pesticides are bad for humans (cancer-causing, even) unless you can advance some proof. So we are rather stuck. Meanwhile, odd things sometimes occur. A few years ago a lot of broiler chicks, mainly in the United States and Scandinavia, began to die. No one could find a virus or bacillus, nor any other cause to account for an accumulation of fluid in the heart sac and damage to kidneys and livers; so it was labelled chick oedema, which simply means swelling. A smart piece of detective work traced the trouble to a fat in the chick's mash which contained an active poison—so active, indeed, that one part in twenty million killed the little birds. This poison was in turn traced back to the residues of a chlorinated hydrocarbon pesticide. The interesting part was that the poisonous elements in those pesticides, however mixed and treated in a laboratory, had no ill effects upon chicks. Something happened to them in the chicks' body—what, no one could say. The poison also damaged the livers of monkeys; yet it couldn't be detected by the finest available tests.

Then there was the Smarden affair, which may perhaps bear a brief recapitulation. In January, 1963, a man employed in the Rentokil factory near Tenterden, in Kent, brought a Labrador puppy to his local veterinary surgeon, Mr Douglas Good. The pup was having fits and eventually died. Four months later, inexplicably and suddenly, a local farmer lost five sheep. Soon afterwards, Mr Good took a walk along a stream that rose near the factory, and noticed that the vegetation along its banks was black and dead. He sent the water off to be analysed. Next day he was called to a convulsive goat whose owner worked in the factory. The Kent River Board then had all the ditches and ponds near the factory fenced off. Despite this, one of the farmers, Mr Jull, lost several cows and others became easily tired, given to panting if made to hurry, and sparing with their milk. Several of their calves died. In July, a team of chemists from the de le Warr laboratories in Oxford detected in the water traces of fluoroacetamide, an ingredient of certain rat poisons, including one manufactured at the Rentokil factory. The quantities were less than is often to be found in tea, but they were in a different and far more deadly chemical form.

Then, one by one, Mr Jull's cows began to die. By September, from a herd of twenty-six, only eleven survived. Their carcases poisoned several dogs, so the rest of the herd was destroyed and the ashes of their funeral pyres buried eight feet underground.

By now, everyone was alerted. The Rentokil factory pumped water from the ditches and ponds and took it out to sea. Mr Jull, his farm totally denuded of animals, spent his time scrubbing out his buildings. (Despite the reputation of farmers for grousing, apparently he never complained—"a wonderful character," Mr Good commented.) In December, the sale of fluoroacetamide rat-poisons was banned, except for its use by local authorities in sewers. (One-twentieth of an ounce of poison is enough to kill 1,200 dogs, terrier size.) The factory stopped making fluoroacetamides and dumped the waste products out at sea. It is a sidelight on the contaminated state of these islands that a special ship exists whose sole job it is to deposit in the long-suffering ocean these various waste products, mostly radio-active, of our industries. The water's "priestlike task of pure ablution round earth's human shores" must be getting difficult.

Minute amounts of fluoroacetamide will kill animals, there is no cure or antidote and—most disturbing of all—no trace of it was detected in any of the dead beasts. What happened to it when it got into their bodies? Did the chemistry of metabolism, working in the living test-tube of the animal, turn it into something else? Have any other rivers, streams, ponds and ditches been contaminated? How long does such contamination last? Can any humans have suffered from fluoroacetamide poisoning disguised as something else—heart trouble, possibly, or just, like Mr Jull's cows, being tired and out of breath? We live longer now, and diagnose diseases better; and something is bound to get us in the end. "It is by chemistry that we breed, grow, survive, work and eventually must die", an eminent chemist, Dr E. F. Edson, has written. The questions how, when, and why, remain.

Pearls before Swine

ONE-QUARTER of all the piglets born in this country die before they are weaned at eight weeks old. Some are crushed by clumsy mothers, some die of cold, or from anaemia which can be prevented, but others from disease. "Pigs are queer things," say the people who keep them; they die unaccountably; and a great many suffer from disease. The diseases do not always kill them, but do greatly reduce their efficiency as meal-into-meat converters, which means that they take longer, and cost more than they need, to turn into pork or bacon.

So the concept of the pathogen-free pig has come into being. Every newborn piglet enters the world with a host of pathogens inside it, ready to take advantage of the least weakening of resistance in their host to multiply and produce clinical symptoms of disease. So the piglet walks a knife-edge between health and sickness. The idea of the pathogen-free pig is simple. Instead of strengthening the young pig's ability to fight back, by adding antibiotics to its ration and giving it the best possible environment, could not the pathogens be kept out of its body altogether? Hence the application of hysterectomy to sows, a technique evolved in the United States and practised here on an increasing scale since 1957.

The farmer sends his pregnant sow to one of two Cambridge firms whose veterinary surgeons extract her womb just before her piglets would otherwise have been born. (The sow herself is killed.) They pop each piglet into a separate sterilised, stainless-steel incubator and rear it on a sterile diet in air that is filtered three times. For their first fourteen days, the piglets inhabit a world of maximum anti-germ security—filtered air, antiseptics, controlled temperatures, automatic feeding and all the hygiene of a modern operating theatre. At a fortnight old they move to broiler cages, still closely guarded from germs for another month, when they are ready to be sent to the farm.

Meanwhile, the farmer has carried out a drastic spring-cleaning. First, he must clear out all his existing pigs; then he must clean, disinfect, and generally go over his buildings with a fine toothcomb to destroy every micro-organism on the place, or else—more satisfactorily—erect insulated, germ-proof new buildings to take his minimal-disease pigs, as they are called nowadays in preference to pathogen-free.

All this costs a lot of money. To make it worth while, minimal-disease piglets must grow more quickly and economically than their microbe-infested brethren; fewer should die, and in due course their descendants should replace our disease-ridden porcine population, and give us better pork and bacon at a lower cost. Experiments in Oxfordshire showed a fifteen per cent improvement in conversion rates over normal pigs, combined with lower losses from disease. The SPF programme, as it is called there—Specific Pathogen Free—is going ahead fast in the United States and in Canada, where one-quarter of the country's pork is already produced by this method, and it is reckoned that, barring accidents, within ten years nearly all will come from SPF hogs.

Allied with a programme to breed better, as well as healthier, pigs, the hope is to lop about six weeks off the time it takes to turn a piglet into meat. "At present," a geneticist said, "tens of thousands of tons of fat are thrown away every year, and with them much of the feeding value and nearly all the flavour. Rather than see the fat thrown into the dustbin, we want to breed it out of the pig." So there are to be leaner pigs, as well as quicker growing ones, if the geneticists are successful.

In time, a herd is bound to get re-infected, and then the farmer has to clear it out and start all over again. Is the game worth the candle? "It is too early yet to say. The Americans reckon that if you can keep disease out for three to five years, you get your money back." In other senses, the bugs are not yet out of the system. Some minimal disease pigs have developed weakness in their back legs, perhaps due to rearing them in wire cages. But this, too, may be bred out.

There are other ways of trying to overcome the pathogens, one of which carries matters to an opposite extreme. This is the sweat-box system pioneered by Mr James Jordan of County Down, and now widely used in Northern Ireland.

Sweat-box pigs live more or less in Turkish baths, and generate the heat themselves. Pigs, incidentally, do not sweat, but the sweat-box walls stream with moisture. The temperature rises to eighty-five or ninety degrees. Everything depends on packing the pigs in so tightly that they themselves create and maintain this high temperature and humidity. Far from finding this distressing, it appears to make them thrive.

Pigs in a sweat-box brought to my mind a hippopotamus wallow, near the Murchison Falls in Uganda, where thousands of blubbery, glistening bodies were packed together, like a mass of pinkish-grey bubbles, half-submerged in swamp and mud. Hippos make their own open-air sweat-boxes. Pigs dwell in chambers sixteen feet by eight, each of which holds twenty-five baconers. This allows five square feet of floor space to each pig.

Food and rest occupy their lives. "To rise and eat, then lie and sleep! What then? To rise and eat, then lie and sleep again!" It looks dreadful, but remains true that pigs, when allowed the choice, behave much like hippos; they cluster together in close-packed, cheek-by-jowl heaps. Put half a dozen shelters in a field and you will find all the pigs on top of one another in one of them, the other shelters almost empty. Pigs are ultra-gregarious.

It is also true that, in sweat-boxes, they have hitherto kept remarkably free from diseases, especially those of the respiratory passages, such as virus pneumonia and rhinitis, which are exceedingly common among fattening pigs. No one is sure of the reason. Possibly globules of moisture surround and imprison the viruses, but that is only a theory. Dr Gordon of Stormont, near Belfast, has counted the bacteria in sweat-boxes and found that numbers fall as humidity rises. Some years before, a similar co-relation was discovered in submarines: the cook's mess, where humidity was high, harboured fewer bacteria than the deck, where it was low. And some years before that, to be precise in 1771, Arthur Young described a system of fattening oxen practised by a Mr Moody of Retford, who believed that the hotter they were kept, the faster they would fatten, and "accordingly keeps them shut up and, for some time, does not so much as let in any air through the holes in the doors; the breath of so many, with the natural heat of their bodies, brings them soon to sweating prodigiously, and, when this is at its height, they fatten the best and quickest."

The fact is that pigs seem to thrive on high humidity but not on dust and dryness, which the sweat-box has been designed to avoid. Their food arrives in pipes, in liquid form, controlled by a lever in a mixing shed. The pigman never need enter the sweat-box unless there is a sick animal. The housing cost works out at about £6 a pig. Next door is what the owner called a "gold-plated piggery" put up at a cost of £25 a pig. He is comparing the two systems, and so far the food-into-flesh conversion rate is almost exactly the same.

There is nothing new, of course, in keeping pigs indoors. As they have always been shut up in styes to fatten, intensive methods have not radically changed their lives. "Our modern breeds of pig," an expert told me, "are descended from two wild stocks: one from Northern Europe and the other from Asia, probably Malaya. This was a swamp and forest dwelling animal, with a snout evolved to dig up roots and tubers. Its descendants still like rootling and dislike direct sunlight. To the extent that sweat-boxes are moist, warm and fairly dark, they are in line with what a pig thrives on. When pigs have pneumonia and coughing fits, they can't be very happy. So if health is any guide, this system is reasonable."

The fact that many pigs take to biting off each others' tails whenever they are crowded and confined—not necessarily, or more than elsewhere, in sweat-boxes— suggests some maladjustment: boredom, most pig-keepers think, possibly aggravated by skin parasites. (Feeding cassava meal has also been blamed.) One man stopped it, temporarily at any rate, by throwing in a bit of straw for his pigs to play with; another, a few lumps of coal. A "maladjusted" pig which allows itself to be bullied by the boss pigs may get its tail bitten off. Good pigmen isolate such weaker brethren at the first sign of bullying. Under any system of intensive management, troubles that are not nipped in the bud are apt to grow at an alarming rate and spread like an epidemic.

Are sweat-boxes cruel? Or, indeed, any method of fattening pigs that crowds them in together with nothing to do but eat, sleep and put on weight? No intensive method *looks* attractive: mountains of close-packed flesh, animals without freedom of choice to pick and seek out their food, mere bodies that convert meal into meat to feed you and me, and die before they reach maturity. Given all that, the particular conditions of the sweat-box do not appear to cause any *extra* distress.

It is quite true that pigs enjoy warmth, moisture and propinquity. Would they also enjoy freedom? Freedom to do what? In a state of nature to seek their food. If the food is provided, what need is there to seek it? As in, perhaps, the ultimate welfare state? Has freedom any further value than that? What do we know of the psychological discomfort that could be caused by stress due to overcrowding? More questions to which there are no answers. Meanwhile the pigs are warm, moist, and well-fed.

The King of Love My Shepherd Is

EVERYWHERE that Mary went, her lamb was bound to go—indoors, of course. Sheep are on their way, if as yet only in small numbers, to barn and cubicle, shelter under roofs instead of rocks, to drink from troughs instead of burns.

From an intensive viewpoint, sheep are unsatisfactory. They share with the cow a low rate of reproduction, seldom having more than two offspring a year. And the rate at which they convert vegetation into meat is poor. On the other hand, certain breeds thrive on the poor vegetation, low in feeding value, to be found on hills, and have become adapted to cold, wet and generally severe mountain climates. About one-quarter of the land of Britain consists of hill grazing that cannot, generally speaking, be ploughed or exploited as the lowland pastures are.

Could better use be made by better sheep of all this rough grazing, we could step up our meat consumption despite a world shortage of beef. Whereas each one of us eats, on average, just over nine ounces of beef and veal a week, we eat less than seven ounces of lamb and mutton. (That is the British average: the Welsh eat more lamb and mutton than beef, but the Scots nearly three times as much beef; country people eat more beef and pigmeat than city-dwellers, but less lamb and mutton; Londoners eat more meat of every kind than anyone else.)

So sheep must be persuaded, like pigs and poultry, to convert food into flesh more efficiently. The first stage is to find out just how good, or bad, at this they are, and so there is an experimental flock of ewes that are being milked by machine, in order that their milk can be exactly weighed and analysed. While the ewes soon get used to machines designed to fit their udders, which have only two teats, they obstinately cling to a large proportion of their milk, whose "let-down" is controlled by a hormone called oxytosin released into the bloodstream by the pituitary gland. So, in order to bring these ewes into line, they are given a shot of oxytosin twice a day in their jugular veins, inserted by means of small plastic tubes called canulae.

Next door, their lambs are put to the test to measure the rate of which they convert their food into meat. These lambs can be as awkward as their mothers. Warm and comfortable in pens, with plenty of good food, some of these unaccountably started dying, without any trace of a pathogenic infection. Eventually, a strange thing was diagnosed: copper poisoning. Yet the lambs had access to no source of copper beyond the very small traces normally put into all balanced rations. These lambs had been hoarding this copper in their livers, and then, even more mysteriously, suddenly releasing it. They had killed themselves with copper, unconsciously committed suicide. Why, or how, no one knows.

Commercially, more and more ewes are being wintered indoors. A Cambridgeshire farmer who keeps about three hundred in a barn has satisfied himself that his ewes eat less, put on more weight and lamb more prolifically than when they winter in the fields. "They lamb in the dry—so much better for the shepherd. And we get no losses due to wet." They soon give up panicking when people walk about amongst them, and the farmer is able to keep more sheep on the same amount of land because his grass, instead of being trampled and muddy, gets away to a flying start in the spring.

When it comes to stepping up productivity by having larger families, ewes are more co-operative than cows. There are breeds of sheep already in existence which do not stop at twins, or even triplets, but quite often have litters of four, five or even six lambs. As these breeds are small, skinny and light in the fleece, hitherto no one has paid them much attention; now it is realised that they carry a priceless genetic inheritance. The most promising breed appears to be the Landrace from Finland. Why Finnish sheep should be so startlingly prolific, no one knows.

The British Dorset Horn variety lambs early, around Christmas, and can sometimes be induced to have a second family later in the year. At Edinburgh, Finnish ewes crossed with Dorset Horn rams are producing "lamb litters", five or six in number, which show such promise that there is talk, if not yet above a whisper, of a genetic break-through. And Mr Oscar Colburn, who farms in Gloucestershire, has evolved a new breed of sheep, the Colbred, for which high conversion rates, quick growth, fecundity and other virtues are claimed. With the aid of a computer, and following techniques evolved by poultry breeders, it is being crossed with an even more prolific breed called the Romanoff. Sheepmen believe that in a decade or so Britain's flocks will consist of one or two new breeds turning out as much meat, or more, as the old ones from the same quantity of food, and giving birth to at least twice as many lambs.

The last to be affected will be the hill sheep, because they cannot come indoors if they are to make use of the coarse, tufty grasses, the heather and bracken and the rest of the poor vegetation of the mountains and fells. Their way of life upon their mountainsides, in particular the way they organise themselves as social beings, is turning out to be a lot more complicated than anyone had previously supposed. Say you put a flock of 150 ewes on to a "heft" of about 350 acres, a heft being a particular stretch of hill. As the sheep scatter over the hillside, each ewe stakes out a claim to her own bit of territory, with her lamb by her side.

You might suppose her choice of pasture to be haphazard, but here we have the peck order and the bunt order over again. The vegetation of a pasture varies according to the type of soil on which it grows. Some types support a sweeter, more nutritious sward than others. The lambs whose mothers secure the best ranges naturally grow larger, and more quickly, than lambs whose mothers must make do with vegetation growing on poorer, more acid, rushier or rockier soils.

There is a flock in Scotland being studied through an ingenious instrument called a sheeposcope invented by Mr Robert Hunter, a lifelong student of the behaviour of hill sheep. This flock grazes on a heft which has four types of vegetation, and is split into four corresponding social groups. Each ewe has a "home range" where mothers and daughters stick together; and a lamb will "inherit" her mother's portion of the heft. So, in each home range, a family group builds up, and all the ewes within each social group are related. The flock is taken off the heft in winter, but in the spring each sheep resumes her own particular home range. Thus a hill pasture is not just a stretch of hill grazed randomly by sheep: in the words of Mr Hunter it is a "home range in which each range is fenced from the others by the social behaviour of the sheep".

Suppose a shepherd puts out rock-salt for his charges, or carries them some hay at lambing time. He will be wrong if he assumes that each ewe will get an equal share. The "owners" of the range where he deposits his salt or hay will have the lot. Often there is an area of common ground, bordering a pathway dividing the ranges, along which any sheep may travel, and the best way to ensure fair shares is for the shepherd to deposit his salt or hay on these "roads of access".

Sheep will tend to crowd on to the better ranges and sometimes, therefore, over-graze them. But just to remove some of the whole flock, in the belief that you are lightening the load on their food supplies, will seldom answer. If you move sheep whose home-range does not coincide with the over-grazed part of the heft, you will provide no remedy.

So the principle of social status, the familiar hierarchy ranging from the boss down to the dogsbody, has an ecological as well as a social purpose. The meeker, less aggressive ewes must seek out more distant pastures. This scatters the flock over the whole heft, instead of encouraging all its members to concentrate in one place which they will over-graze. More remains to be found out before we understand it all, and perhaps not much time left to find it out in, if sheep are to follow hens, pigs and calves into pen and barn. This complex social life and physical dispersal based on order, degree and rank, will no longer be possible in the slatted, sealed and darkened sheep-shed and the close-packed lamb-lot where our future flocks may be confined. Here they will be fed by automation on rations designed by a computer for the supermarket trade; and the shepherd with his skill, his patience and endurance, lambing his ewes by the light of lanterns in a bitter north-east wind, will soon be as obsolete as milkmaid and chimney-sweep, wheelwright and weaver. No doubt he will be replaced by the skilled sheep technician equipped with a slide-rule in place of a crook, and trained to set a thermostat rather than to trim a wick. As for the sheep, no more starving in snowdrifts, getting swept away by floods or drowning in burns; snug, sheltered and anonymous, they will be warm, dry, and well fed.

Whiter than White

THE Dutch system of intensive calf rearing started in about 1955. At first it was a grim business. Calves were confined in solid boxes with lids, and could not even lie down. They suffered from anaemia, swollen joints and, one must suppose, utter misery.

This did not last long, at least in that extreme form, in Holland, and was never practised in Britain. The box became a crate, at first with solid sides, then slatted. The superstition that darkness whitens the flesh of calves, as it does in the case of celery or seakale, was exploded. Research belatedly discovered that, in the words of a leading authority, Dr T. j. Bakker, "The food conversion rate and live-weight increase per day are exactly the same in complete darkness, subdued light, and bright light. It does not make any difference if the calf is kept completely immobile, or if it is given sufficient room to move about."

Nowadays it is unlikely that any calves reared on the intensive method in this country are kept in total darkness. Subdued light is favoured, and said to be more discouraging to flies than light at full strength. "We like sufficient light to read a newspaper," Dr Bakker said, and this was the case in the units I visited in Dorset. Each calf was in a slatted crate, could see around it, communicate with other calves and lie down; but it could not turn round.

The floor is slatted to allow dung to fall through on to concrete and get sluiced away, and so the calves keep pretty clean. Wire mesh has been tried, but proved uncomfortable, and I was told it had been given up. It is impossible to check statements like these. It is true that animals who fret do not thrive, and calves *must* thrive in order to put on up to two and a half pounds a day. If they keep this up they are ready for slaughter, at 260 to 300 lb live-weight, in twelve weeks—only a little longer than a broiler chicken. The intensive veal producer must finish four batches a year to make it pay.

So deeply embedded in all calves is the instinct to suck that, if no cow is available, they will suck each other; it is to avoid this that they are kept in separate crates. Some producers risk the sucking and put three or four calves together. So far, no differences in health and growth-rate have shown up as between the two methods. "You have got to keep the calf contented and comfortable whatever the method, or it will not thrive," a producer said. "The conversion rate is about the highest in the world, one pound of food to 1·3 lb of flesh, and it is easily upset. Unhappy calves become nervous and panic at the least little thing, say a dropped bucket, or even a bird flying in. You can see for yourself how quiet these calves are."

This was true. Although a stranger, they paid me no particular attention and showed no signs of flinching or of panic when I walked about. They were concentrating upon their meal, a milk substitute served at exactly the right temperature and in the right quantities, according to each calf's age and weight. Calves have delicate digestive systems, easily deranged, especially by over-feeding. In earlier days a lot died, either from forms of pneumonia or from digestive upsets. Strict hygiene plus very careful feeding reduces the second, hygiene plus ventilation the first. Fans keep the air in constant motion, and a certain level of humidity must be maintained—more important than temperature, for calves dislike dry air. All this is highly skilled and needs unremitting attention. A successful veal producer observed:

"No two calves are alike. You have got to know each one personally, its individual likes and dislikes." You would scarcely have thought a calf would have much chance to express likes and dislikes in its separate crate, but the owner appeared to know each one apart, together with its age and history.

Intensive producers of any type of animal live almost in a state of siege. Armed with antiseptics and antibiotics, ventilators and syringes, synthetic hormones and time-switches and suction pumps, the commander keeps at bay a host of unseen micro-organisms at work with unrelenting energy to destroy his animals. The struggle never stops and never can; as units get bigger, and more dependent on an absolute control of the environment, so does the intensity of the struggle and the risk involved.

Some think intensive units will not get much bigger for this very reason; in fact, there might even be a trend the other way. A limit there must somewhere be. As humans hand over more and more of their traditional activities to machines, the risk of major breakdowns both increases and becomes more dangerous. A serious power cut could, tomorrow, kill calves in thousands, and fowls in hundreds of thousands. And there are bound to be breakdowns in management.

One day, perhaps, someone will invent an electronic stockman; forewarned by the look in a calf's eye, or the droop of a pig's tail, it will flash a light to signal some impending ailment, or soothe a nervous creature by the click of its valves. A farmer of my acquaintance can tell when a sow is coming into season simply by resting his hand on her back; how this works, he cannot explain. Until the electronic stockmaster is with us, we still need humans, and if they are too thin on the ground we take appalling risks.

There are other snags in the development of intensive production. One is, what to do with all the dung. In Holland, where the average holding is about ten acres, it has already become the limiting factor. What are we to do in our own congested island? When a 10,000 barley-beef unit near Stowmarket comes into production, its managers will face the problem of disposing every year of somewhere in the region of 10,000 tons of manure. Already dung disposal is a major headache for producers of broilers and battery hens. The management of one big unit that I visited pays a contractor to dump it in an old gravel pit.

This seems a very wasteful way to treat a highly concentrated source of soil fertility, but when it accumulates in such great concentration there is far too much for local use, and transport costs do not justify its being sent long distances.

As men and beasts increasingly coagulate, the disposal of their wastes will become a matter of increasing urgency, scarcely to be dealt with indefinitely by dumping it in quarries, flushing it into the sea or plastering it, in the raw, over our diminishing fields, there to contaminate our soil and water. Here and there a little seed of common sense has germinated. The city of Leicester is building, at a cost of some £4 million and after four years experiment, a plant to convert the sludge from its sewage works, mixed with its domestic refuse, into a marketable compost, packed with nutriments enriching to the soil. When completed, this will be the largest plant of its kind in Europe. Why only Leicester? Others will no doubt follow its lead, so long as the process proves successful. But we advance, on these matters, if at all, at the pace of the snail, when that of the greyhound is needed.

If, on the score of cruelty, people worry less about

71

veal calves than battery hens, it is only because there are fewer of them; the principle is just the same. They are prisoners, cabined and confined. No green fields, no sunlight, no mother love. It is true they are not as over-crowded, but on the other hand they are higher in the scale of intelligence, so probably more liable to suffer from feelings of frustration and stress. A calf penned into a narrow crate is no worse off, better off in most cases, than a calf tied up night and day in a dark, dirty corner of a draughty, fly-infested shed on a traditional farm, perhaps neglected and ill-fed by a traditional farmer. The only difference is that while the traditional farmer might have half a dozen, his intensive colleague has a hundred or more.

The most dubious aspect of intensive veal production is feeding for white flesh. It is said that calves are deliberately made anaemic by a diet low in iron, the element which provides the source of haemoglobin in their blood.

The story is a complex one. Calves fed entirely on their mother's milk will become anaemic; milk sub-stitute has more iron in it than the natural product, which the calf supplements with grass or hay containing iron; calves reared intensively, denied the grass, must look wholly to the substitute.

Every calf is born with a certain reserve of iron, deposited in the liver of the embryo. This "bank" varies widely from calf to calf. That is one reason why some thrive better than others. Those born with very low iron reserves may develop symptoms of anaemia: loss of appetite, trembling, distress, death in extreme cases. This is one of the hazards a stockman must watch for, and correct with iron supplements when necessary.

Veal consumers insist on white flesh. (They prefer their eggs and beef dark, their veal and sugar light—

why?) This is a matter of feeding. When haemoglobin builds up to a certain level in the blood the calf starts to form, and deposit in its muscles, a substance called myoglobin. This is a reserve; it is red, and darkens the meat. Therefore, the calf must be so fed that it will not have any surplus haemoglobin in its blood to tuck away in its muscles in the form of myoglobin. This is very difficult, because no two calves are alike.

The iron content of water varies, too. When intensive veal production was introduced from Holland, a Dutch firm supplied a milk substitute whose iron content was balanced to match the water of Holland. The calf was supposed to get just enough iron to keep it healthy, but not enough to enable it to form myoglobin in meat-darkening quantities. Then things started to go wrong. Some calves died, others lost their appetites and did not thrive. When the water was analysed, it was found to contain much less iron than the Dutch water; in some cases, no iron at all; the calves were therefore suffering from anaemia. When more iron was put into the substitute, they were all right.

To maintain this balance is a very delicate business, calling for a high degree of skill in management. Calves born with low reserves of iron are liable to suffer from anaemia, while those with high reserves will fail to make the grade for whiter-than-whiteness and displease the consumer. So the average veal calf, while apparently healthy and thriving, has nevertheless a mild, suppressed form of anaemia.

Does this amount to cruelty? To judge from the calves I have seen, and of course I have seen only a very small proportion, they are not, by reason of their haemoglobin levels, in any discomfort, let alone pain. They do not, after all, take any exercise, and there are plenty of humans with low haemoglobin counts who live perfectly

73

normal, healthy lives. But the health of these calves is poised upon a knife-edge. Faulty management can easily tumble them over, and no doubt sometimes does. Then they lose their appetite and feel miserable, and the producer loses his profits and feels miserable too. One producer said: "Anaemic calves won't fatten quickly, so our profits go. Our whole effort is directed towards keeping our calves healthy, and the basis of health is proper feeding. If they were not contented, they would not put on weight."

You hear a lot of this type of argument—as among poultrymen. A distressed, unhappy animal mopes and loses appetite; if it is feeding well, then it is all right. Appetite is largely regulated by hormones manufactured in a small gland at the base of the brain called the hypothalamus. Experimental rats whose hypothalamus was tinkered with by expert surgeons developed such an uncontrolled appetite, and gorged themselves so grossly, that in a few hours they ate their own weight in food and could no longer move. Were *they* happy? Who knows?

The crated calves I saw did not *look* unhappy; glossy of coat, bright of eye, well ventilated, clean, free of flies. On the other hand, they did not look as happy as a pair of calves, free and shiny, who were scampering about a field, kicking up their heels and butting mother's udder when they felt inclined. In part, our judgements are aesthetic; most indoor husbandry is unattractive to the eye.

You cannot rear an animal successfully unless you are fond of it. Your achievement is a quiet, contented, unafraid creature that lets you scratch its back and rub its nose. Then it will grade out firm and lean when it is stunned, bled and hung on a hook. Stockmanship is love, really, carried sometimes to a point of great devotion; its frequent aim, the slaughter of the beloved.

The Stalled Ox

THE Romans picked their swineherds for the sweet-ness of their voices, but thought a cattleman's voice should be gruff to mark his status as the father-figure of the herd. "They were right," a modern stockman commented. "The human voice is terribly important. Every animal knows it and responds. An even pitch will soothe a nervous beast. If I walk through a bunch of cattle, the ones at the bottom of the bunt order walk just in front of me, where they feel safe from being butted by those higher up in the scale."

Now that cattle, like most other edible creatures, have joined the trek towards the great indoors, this ancient link between man and beast is being greatly weakened. It is difficult to mechanise, unless you put the stockman's voice on tape and play it over at intervals, gruff and paternal, to the calves in their pens munching barley and putting on two pounds a day. Their feeding is mechanised already in a modern beef-lot and there's nothing, in theory, to prevent their being left alone from Friday to Monday, listening to the tape, while the stockman has his free weekend.

In 1964, one-fifth of our home-grown beef came from cattle kept indoors all their lives, fed almost wholly on barley and killed when they were about a twelvemonth old. The rest were reared traditionally, in the main on grass, green in summer and stored for winter use as hay or silage, and they were not ready for slaughter until about two years old. The barley-beef system has halved the time it takes to get a beast to the butcher's, and freed the producer from the limits previously set to his production by the size of his farm. The project, started in Suffolk, to keep 10,000 barley-fed calves in a single unit, is only a pilot scheme; if it works, the company envisages several beef-lots with 30,000 beasts in each.

The idea was born in the United States, where it was based on feeding maize, and failed; too many animals got bloat (acute wind) and died. Then Dr T. R. Preston at the Rowett Institute near Aberdeen tried barley, and it worked. The idea caught on quickly—the traditional conservatism among British farmers seems to have evaporated.

The method does not always lower the cost or increase the quantity of beef available—sometimes the opposite, in fact, because output is limited by the number of calves born every year, and a barley-beef weighs less at slaughter, and yields less meat, than a more mature beast reared in the traditional way. But this young, tender flesh that can be packaged for the supermarket just suits the modern housewife. We are eating seventeen pounds more beef a head than we did ten years ago, and demand is rising as our affluence enables us to afford a diet richer in proteins.

Having got the calves on to barley, the next thing is to grow more of it, and this we are doing. Supply rises to meet demand, and advances both in growing and in storing cereals match the need. Damp grain, as everyone knows, does not keep, and as we live in a damp climate, in most years our grain has to be dried. The cost of this probably amounts to about £4 a ton. A farmer-cum-engineer from Staffordshire, Mr I. J. Friend, has pioneered a system that, he believes—some others do not agree—will send the mechanical drier into limbo along with carthorses, pitchforks and milking stools.

He puts his wet barley straight into silos, which he seals; no drying, no handling, no outlay except for the storage silo, which is expensive. The grain keeps free from moulds, and emerges smelling faintly of beer. The whole trick is to make the silo absolutely airtight; some are lined with fibre glass. Then yeasts which develop naturally on grain use up all the oxygen, and leave a high concentration of carbon dioxide, an excellent preservative for living matter. (Apples have been stored in carbon dioxide for years.) Instead of installing a lot of machinery and burning up a lot of fuel, the grower lets natural yeasts do the job, free. Barley, wet or dry, makes up eighty-five per cent of the beasts' ration; the rest consists of protein-rich feed. If all goes well, the beast goes off for slaughter before it is a year old. Now there is pressure to reduce this time still farther, if possible; and so sex hormones come into play.

Cockerels have been caponised for years by implanting in their necks tablets of a female hormone which makes them fatten quicker and put on leaner flesh, and flesh in the right places. The same with steers. To implant hexoestrol in the bullocks' ears about ninety days before slaughter is now common practice. These oestrogens—female hormones—are made synthetically. Although their effects on the body seem exactly the same as those of natural hormones, there is one important difference: nature's oestrogens quickly break down and disappear, synthetic ones do not, or do so much more slowly. They are apt to hang around, resistant even to cooking. Oestrogens are potent substances, liable, if they are carelessly handled, to induce in human males squeaky voices, beardless chins and swelling breasts. In female domestic animals they can cause cystic ovaries, prolapse of the rectum and nymphomania, so they might not be good for the girls.

Is there, then, a risk that all those succulent little steaks wrapped in polythene in their handy trays are loaded with synthetic hormones that are going to play old harry with our sex? The authorities, as usual soothing (like the stockman's voice), say that all but a tiny fragment of the hexoestrol stays where it is put, in the bullock's ear, and we do not eat ears; second, that only a tiny proportion of the stuff the animal *does* draw from its ear, say one-fiftieth, is retained in its flesh. The rest is excreted or comes to rest in the liver, and we would have to eat livers every day for ten years to register the least effect. American scientists have found less than one part in ten million in the edible portions of implanted chickens, and one part in a hundred million in implanted beef. So not to worry about our sex.

If these synthetic oestrogens are so indestructible, what happens to the residue? It must go somewhere. What becomes of all the cockerels' necks and bullocks' ears? If they get turned into meat-and-bone meal, will they not find their way back into animals again? There was the case of the sterile mink, who *did* eat meal incorporating cockerels' necks. They stopped breeding, and their owner sued, successfully, for damages. True, we do not eat meat-and-bone meal, but we eat animals that do, and a lot of the tiniest little mickles make a muckle in the end.

Some of the residue must get out on to the land with the dung. What happens next? Does it get into earthworms and disorganise *their* sex life? (They are hermaphrodites.) Go through sewage plants and into ditches and rivers and reservoirs and thence into you and me?

Everything produced by living organisms, and every living organism itself, is in the course of time broken down into its component parts, to be used by other living organisms to build their tissues. This is the great chain of being: more scientifically, the ecosystem. Bacteria and fungi of innumerable kinds are the main agents of this everlasting process. Among them are many specialists which deal with certain substances, and no others; there is even a bacillus that lives on petroleum oil. Many man-made creations, as distinct from those produced by nature, are broken down by micro-organisms in the same way. But not all. Is there a risk that these may, by their persistence, damage human health? Scientists have not yet probed deep enough to come up with the answer; but some have doubts, for instance that "the long-continued ingestion of small amounts of synthetic oestrogens might be carcinogenic". In other words that these doses, tiny as they are, might in the long run encourage cancer. After "prolonged oestrogen administration at a high level", mice have developed cancer of the breast, and rabbits cancer of the womb. Synthetic oestrogens are known to affect profoundly the structure and reproduction of the body's cells, but no one knows exactly how, or whether little tiny doses taken for years and years can accumulate in the human body to a point where they increase the "carcinogenic load".

Cancer is on the increase, as everyone knows. Synthetic oestrogens are on the increase too; so are diesel fumes, smoking, smog, pesticides, stress, lead, sulphur, molybdenum, radio-active residues and many other things. It is impossible to pin responsibility on to any one of these factors, or even on to all of them combined. And so uneasiness prevails—more acutely, it would seem, among panicky foreigners than in our own phlegmatic land. In the United States, no manufacturer may incorporate synthetic oestrogens into feedingstuffs without a licence; no new licences are issued; and stilboestrol implants into cockerels have been stopped. In France, since 1959, the sale of human foods derived from animals to which oestrogens have been administered has been prohibited; in Sweden, implantations in cattle are banned; in 1961 an order was introduced in Denmark making it illegal to give synthetic oestrogens in any form to any domestic animal. In the Federal Republic of Germany, the law forbids the implanting of oestrogenic substances into animals, or their addition to feeding stuffs. Our native land has no such restrictions.

In its early days, barley-beef production ran into several troubles, mainly concerned with the health of the animals. Quite a lot died of bloat, and quite a lot went blind. Bloat is now controlled by feeding the barley in a coarser form, and by adding a little hay or straw to the diet. The blindness was due to lack of vitamin A, which can be easily added to the ration. Lack of sunlight does not seem to matter, so far as anyone knows. Nowadays well-managed barley-fed calves look sleek and healthy; as a rule they are kept in pens containing anything from ten or a dozen up to twenty-five or thirty, often in converted barns, so they are not isolated like quality veal calves, and can turn round and walk about. If life is not exactly stimulating for them, at least it is not downright uncomfortable.

But quite a lot develop liver trouble. Of some three hundred carcases examined at the Rowett Institute, one-third had abscessed livers, and over one-half diseased kidneys. There are two theories about this. One is that a diet of barley, so low in bulky roughage for which the ruminant's digestive system was designed, fails to maintain the health of the animal, for reasons which are still not understood; livers and kidneys are the first organs to suffer and the trouble would worsen as the animal aged. The other is that, on the contrary, the damage was caused during calfhood, and will get no worse. Calf-rearing is a tricky business best carried out by specialists, and most barley-beef producers do not take sufficient trouble or lack the expertise, for which the calf pays. A vet who held this view explained: "Calves need soft food until the lining of the rumen has developed to deal with harder substances. I have seen young calves given coarse, rolled barley with all the awns and bits of husk in it hard as needles. The result is numerous small stomach ulcers and lesions of kidneys and livers. The stomach ulcers heal in time, but the damage to livers and kidneys has been done." There may, of course, be other causes, still unknown.

Some think that barley-beef will be a passing fashion, because the meat is not as tasty as the flesh of animals reared more slowly out of doors. A supermarket cut of barley-beef is certainly a very pale reflection of a joint of prime Scots beef which has taken perhaps three years a-growing on soil and pasture famous for their beef-producing qualities. As with wine, the quality of beef varies from district to district, even from field to field, as well as from season to season. If we want perfection we will not look to yearlings stuffed with barley in a barn, under-exercised, immature and possibly with an abscessed liver.

But, of course, even if we want perfection, very few of us can hope to find it in a mass-production age, with all these multiplying mouths to feed. Few of us do want it, as a matter of fact. Just as most of us will settle gladly for a bottle of ordinary, cheap country wine, rather than hanker after a Château Lafite or tip-top Montrachet at four times the price, so the great majority of housewives, hurrying home from work to fix a quick meal for the family in front of the telly, wants the tender, convenient, quickly cooked little cut of steak in its oven-ready tray. A prime Scots surloin, expensive to buy and taking hours to cook, is not for her; the ritual of father with the carving knife at the head of the family table is a thing of the past; and no one wants a lot of cold meat cluttering up the refrigerator. For the producer, also, barley beef fits the modern trend. One man can look after many more beasts; feeding can be largely mechanised; more animals can be packed on to much less land; and the system is geared to the mass-production, big-business type of financier, who is gradually replacing Farmer Giles.

All this does not say that, in a few years time, we shall have nothing but barley-beef. There is a lot of land that can be properly used only by the out-door beef herd that will graze pastures unsuited to the growing of cereals. One system does not obliterate the other. No doubt the connoisseur, if he is prepared to pay for it, will continue to enjoy his cut of prime beef accompanied by his Château Lafite; but for the bulk of us, scurrying from factory and office to electric cooker and television screen via the self-service store, our frozen cuts of relatively cheap, uniform and tender barley-beef will meet an expanding and enduring need.

Shall we be able to get enough of them in future, as our numbers grow? Just to keep pace with the increase in our own population, we need an extra 48,000 beef carcases a year; as our standard of living continues to rise, so does the demand for red meat. Where is it all to come from? The beef-lot is the obvious answer; but the beef-lot must be constantly replenished by calves. As we cannot yet make synthetic calves on an assembly line, they have got to come from cows, and the best most cows can manage is a single calf a year. Many fail to manage even that. Our breeding herd numbers about four and a half million cows, who produce annually about 3·35 million calves, and the output cannot suddenly be increased.

The matter is complicated by the fact that barley-beefers only want one kind of animal and that is a Friesian. At a pinch they can do with half-Friesians, the

82

other half as a rule being Charollais or Hereford, but they say no other breed will do. Just over one and a half million Friesian calves are born each year and half of these are females, mostly kept for replacements. Male Friesian calves are a by-product of dairying, and the dairymen are concentrating all their efforts, with considerable success, on getting more milk from fewer cows. This means fewer calves for feed-lots and yards. So we are being pulled in two opposite directions—more calves wanted by the beef-men, and fewer cows needed by the milk-men.

Cows sometimes have twins. If sometimes, why not always, or at any rate more frequently? If more cows could be induced to drop more twins, we could have more calves without keeping more cows.

So we get back to hormones, which control the breeding apparatus of the cow. Normally, a cow's ovaries produce only one egg which, when successfully fertilised, in turn produces one calf. Researchers employed by the Milk Marketing Board have injected several hundred cows with a hormone extract which induced the ovaries to produce more eggs, up to five or six in some cases. That was overdoing things. Two embryos are as much as any normal cow can bring to birth successfully; multiple conceptions lead to dead embryos and abortions. The difficulty is to find a level of hormone dosage that results in two eggs instead of one, but not more than two. If the dose is too weak, the cow fails to respond at all; if too strong, her ovaries shed two or three eggs and the outcome is dead embryos or stillborn calves.

So these experiments failed. But years of work are always needed before a new technique can be evolved to manipulate anything so complicated and old-established as the reproductive system of a cow. And cows are obstinate, conservative creatures. Six out of ten in an experimental bunch kept intensively, on a concentrated diet with no hay, and so managed as to calve before they were two years old, had to be written off before two years were up because of kidney and liver damage, infertility, uterine prolapse, bloat and laminitis in the feet; and over one-third of their calves died.

There are other, and comparatively minor, ways to ameliorate the situation, if not to relieve it. One is to overcome breeding diseases in our dairy cows which hold back calf production, and are getting worse rather than better. Another is to reduce calf mortality. A cunning little by-way round the central obstacle, shortage of beef, has been opened up by chemists who have discovered how to make the toughest beef from ancient cows tender by steeping it in papaine, an extract derived from pawpaw trees.

Could not the dairy farmer keep more cows? He could, of course, but then he would produce more milk, and we do not want more milk, at least in liquid form. Moreover, the dairy farmer has to lower his production costs like everyone else, and by the same means—less labour, more capital, higher output, quicker returns; i.e. intensiveness. The latest development is known as zero grazing, the dairy farmers' counterpart of feed-lot, sweat-box and battery cage. It is based on the same principle, to keep your animals indoors and take the food to them, instead of taking them to the food. While the bullock's food is barley, the cow's is grass, and it is more cumbrous, expensive and difficult to shift, because most of it is water. So you must either dry it first into hay, or take the water along and feed the grass either as silage, or direct to the cow.

The invention of the forage harvester, which mows young grass and blows it into a trailer, has made possible the zero system, which means the cows do not graze at all. Generally they have a yard where they can move about, cubicles inside a shed where they repair to lie down, and a milking parlour. Every morning, in summer, the farmer runs his forage-harvester over a strip of high-yielding grass ley and brings the grass into the yard, where the cows pull it out for themselves. You would think that taking grass to the cow would be more time-and-energy-consuming than taking the cow to the grass, but apparently this is not so: the man is mechanised and the cow is not. It is quicker to run the forage harvester over a strip of grass than to drive cows out and then back again for the afternoon's milking.

The other great advantage is that on the same acreage you can keep more cows, because there is less wastage. The cows do not trample the grass and plaster it with cowpats. Behind the mower goes the spreader putting on nitrogen, up comes another crop of grass, and so on all through the growing season. By these means you achieve a rate of stocking that would have seemed fantastic even ten or fifteen years ago, when a farmer who could milk one cow and rear his replacements on two acres was exceptional. With zero grazing, one cow to one acre is nothing out of the way. This might enable some small farmers to survive the agribusiness age—those, that is, who could raise the large amount of necessary capital, work seven days a week for less money than an unskilled factory hand, deploy a lot of skill and never have a day off through illness.

9

Stress

A SIZEABLE and growing branch of biology is devoted to the study of animal behaviour. In almost every major country, detailed studies of wild and of domestic animals are in train. In time, hard conclusions will emerge, but few as yet; this branch of science is relatively new, the difficulties are great and findings so far mainly tentative.

One conclusion, however, about which there is no argument is that the more we discover about animal behaviour, the more complex, subtle and highly organised, under the surface, does it reveal itself to be.

It was not until 1913 that a researcher called Schjelder-uppe Ebbe first reported the existence of a peck order among poultry. Later still, in 1920, the amateur naturalist Eliot Howard propounded the theory,[1] fore-shadowed as early as the seventeenth century both in Italy and England, that, in the nesting season, each male bird stakes out a claim to its own stretch of territory whose boundaries it proclaims by song, and whose inviolability it defends by aggression. Birds were at first thought to have, in the animal world, a monopoly of this kind of social behaviour. Then came other discoveries, until it now appears that vertibrates of almost every species, if living in communities, have evolved a complex social structure allowing for order and degree, for the principle of leaders and the led, of social discipline, authority and patterns of behaviour which keep a balance not merely between one species and another, and between the species and its environ-

[1] Eliot Howard, *Territory in Bird Life*, Collins (reprinted 1948).

ment, but internally, among the individuals who make up the community. Some insects, notably bees, observe in an even more remarkable fashion this social structure of rank, order and degree. In nature, there is no anarchy.

> *The heavens themselves, the planets and this centre*
> *Observe degree, priority and place,*
> *Insisture, course, proportion, season, form,*
> *Office and custom, in all line of order.*

Not only the heavens with their stars, but the earth with its creatures, whether earwig, owl or seagull, swallow, antelope or vole.

Take, for instance, the Uganda kob. You would think a herd of kob was just a group of several hundred rufous antelopes roaming the sunlit African pastures. Far from it. To begin with, each herd 'owns' a particular area, and will not venture over an invisible line in the bush. Every young male, soon after he is weaned, enters a pool of bachelors from which he must emerge to stake a claim to a particular stretch of territory, usually by driving off an existing owner, more rarely by emigration to a new land.

When he has got his home ready, he sets about getting a wife, or wives, by various means. Sometimes he stands in front of a female and just stares at her, or he may chase her into his territory and try to keep her there. His bit of land is generally about twenty-five or thirty yards across and in it there is a regular resting place, worn almost bare, and a defecating point. If there is an ant hill handy, the kob uses it to rub up his horns. He constantly patrols his territory, dragging his feet on the ground to mark his ownership with his own particular smell. (His feet are equipped with scent-glands.) If he has to leave his plot, he hurries back to make sure no rival is challenging his ownership. Sooner or later, he will go down before a young and vigorous kob and return, disconsolate no doubt, to the pool of males.

By then, his work will be done. Most males who secure territory accumulate harems of three, four, and up to twenty wives; without a territory no male can have a wife at all. Once a harem-owner, the buck struts around with a stiff-legged gait, head up, horns back and teeth bared, cock of the walk. You would never guess all this from seeing a herd of sleek, red-coated, lyre-horned antelope grazing in Uganda's National Parks, and it is only in the last few years that Dr Hal Buechner of Washington State University has found it all out.

In the world of monkeys, the same principles apply. Most apes and monkeys live in bands, each band with its particular territory. The earliest studies, carried out on the inmates of zoos, created in the minds of observers an image of primates as ferocious, brutish creatures given to ceaseless quarrelling as individuals and to fighting as groups. But when biologists got out into the bush and jungle, a wholly different pattern of behaviour was observed. Far from bickering and savaging each other, apes and monkeys appeared amiable in the extreme, invariably polite to strangers and, for instance in the case of gorillas, often bedding down together for the night.

This remarkable contrast between the behaviour of primates in the wild and primates in captivity can be explained in one word: stress. Free animals seldom fight with real savagery, captive ones frequently do—unless the population of the free primates builds up to a density that causes stress to appear. Then the wild ones fight too. In the words of Dr W. M. S. Russell,[1] "virtually no mammals fight violently at moderate population densities in the wild, and virtually all

[1] From talks reprinted in *The Listener* of November 5th and 12th, 1964.

mammals fight violently under population pressure or when crowded in captivity".

Each band has its territory; within each band, each ape its rank. Japanese monkeys have developed this hierarchical sense to such a pitch that observers even talk about a "court" of simian nobles, headed by a president, that moves around escorted by a screen of lower-class males, who do not eat until their superiors have had their fill. The females take their husbands' rank. Social climbers among the males try to ingratiate themselves among high-ranking females by minding the baby when a new one is born. A leader's chief function within the band, like that of a medieval baron, appears to be (at least according to some observers) to stop quarrelling among his henchmen; as between bands, there is plenty of bluff but little action of a violent kind. Bands of howler monkeys simply sit and howl at each other, and the loudest howl wins. "Life in a wild primate band," Dr Russell concludes, "involves little friction and much sociability"; there are close friendships, mutual coat-groomings, teenage play and great parental devotion. Violence has been regulated, and aggression controlled, by the mechanisms of society.

Everything is different in a zoo. Since there is nothing constructive to do, and therefore no chance for individuals to develop their gifts of leadership, there is only one way in which leaders can emerge, and that is by fighting—brute force, by nature repugnant to the brutes but induced by humans. The entire social system of the primates, their organisation into bands to exploit territories, and into rank to avoid strife; the mechanisms which kept their society sweet and sound—all that, in zoos, is swept away. The result is anarchy in which fighting becomes the only way to establish rank. "This brutal method", Dr Russell comments, "does not even work. The wrong monkeys come to the top. Unlike wild leaders, they are insecure and trigger-happy. Unable to assert themselves by a posture of self-assurance, they try to maintain their spurious authority by threats and violence. Government by consent degenerates into an unstable system of 'absolute despotism tempered by assassination'. During a tyrant's brief authority . . . he spends much of his time bullying his subjects. The result is that all the subjects are under ceaseless pressure of attack and threat." Even friendships, coat-groomings, disappear. It all seems sadly familiar. Zoos, Dr Russell reminds us, are urban communities; food is provided in abundance; it is an image of the affluent society. Everyone is warm, dry, and well fed.

What about domestic animals? As we have seen, they too have territories and hierarchical systems. In cattle, this is called the bunt order. There is a boss cow or steer, then lesser bosses who get the next turn at water-trough or feed-hopper, finally the lower orders who take their turn last. Such practices as de-horning, now almost universal among yarded cattle, turn the bunt order upside down. For a while, no one knows who is boss. "De-horning," I was told, "alters the whole personalities of cows; they become much more timid; put any horned animal in among the de-horned, and she will immediately become the boss."

Cows as well as monkeys, it seems, sometimes operate a baby-sitting system, though not with the same object of social advancement. A student of Highland cattle has observed that, when calving time comes round, the last to calve will act as baby-sitter while the other cows go down the hill to be fed. All the small calves stay with her, and she herself may well go hungry for a few days, until the next cow to calve takes her place. Then she goes back into the bottom of the bunt order, and works her way upwards until she resumes the position that she held before.

If we do not yet know, and perhaps never shall, what the animal itself feels about the loss of its own bit of territory—that little empire which, in more natural conditions, it can call its own—we can at least observe how it acts. Take, for instance, the domestic cat, which often reverts to a semi-wild state in those parts of a surviving countryside still only sparsely occupied by humans. Dr Paul Leyhausen, a colleague of Conrad Lorenz, studying such cats in Wales and in Germany, found each male to own a territory having an inner and an outer zone. In the inner zone, the home range, the tom cat rests, feeds, rubs and cleans himself. In the outer range he hunts and courts, and sometimes here encounters other cats whom he does not drive away, so long as it is quite clear who is boss.

Here, in these outer ranges, is a network of paths to be used by all feline visitors; no casual prowling and roaming is permitted. To avoid direct encounters, Dr Leyhausen has written, the cats "follow a definite timetable scheduled like a railway timetable, so as to make collisions unlikely". Sometimes, of course, cats do meet, and then the toms generally fight. Victory confers a right of entry to the loser's territory, but the winner seldom abuses it, and does not drive the loser away. At nightfall, a social gathering, unconnected with mating, sometimes occurs. The cats "just sit around" and groom each other, and there is no fighting at all. ("The only mammal one could conceivably speak of as being socially indifferent," Dr Leyhausen has written, "is a dead one.") The social gathering may continue for several hours, even all night, before each cat disperses to his own bit of ground, where his mate will rear her brood.

The more the ranges fill up with cats, the more

stringent do the rules become, and pretty soon signs of ill-temper appear. When there is plenty of elbow-room, the owners of ranges are tolerant; as pressure mounts, their tolerance wanes. Fights become more common and, says Dr Leyhausen, "pariahs and bullies emerge". Weaker cats are driven off, to go hungry. Dr Leyhausen noted a similar pattern of behaviour in prisoner-of-war camps in Wales and in Canada. Pressure destroys that balance, maintained in all communities, between the social and the solitary habit. In so doing, it distorts behaviour; the strong grow more aggressive, the weak more timid; signs of stress appear.

In rats, mice and other rodents, stress has actually been measured in biochemical terms. When voles were moved into cages containing either hostile strangers, or a lot of fleas, their spleens immediately increased in weight, in some cases from sixty milligrammes to seven hundred milligrammes within a week. A wild rodent overcrowded in captivity will often die as a result of stress. But in the wild state, physical responses to overcrowding may form part of the mechanism that triggers off migrations, as for instance among field mice, voles and lemmings.

Fear and overcrowding increase the weight of rats' adrenal glands. Dr S. A. Barnett of Glasgow University has found that common brown male rats introduced into a cageful of strangers will express their stress by stepping up their output of cortical hormones. Soon they appear bedraggled and feeble, neglect to clean themselves, flinch at the approach of other rats and ultimately die, quite often, without any wound or injury. They die of stress, their blood high in sugar content owing to a failure of the liver. Those who are lowest in the social order are the first to perish, leaving, in some cases, a single dominant male. In overcrowded cages, "alpha" rats emerge to dominate "omega" rats, who often die as a result. In between come "beta" rats who, far from dying, do as they are told, put on weight and survive—collaborators. This sinister grading into bullies, collaborators and proles, linked in some mysterious way with adrenal secretions, does not happen in a state of nature, only when communities become urban in character, over-crowded and confined. The parallels with human destiny are ominous and perhaps too obvious; we are not rats, after all, and should not argue from one species to another. We are all mammals, though.

When you look into it, few species seem to be immune from stress. Guppies and spider-crabs turn cannibal when too closely confined, and red deer stags will kill each other, their calves, and strange hinds. In Minnesota, snowshoe hares, stressed by confinement, were gripped by fatal convulsions, the glycogen content of their livers down to 0·02 per cent instead of a normal 5·5 per cent. These are the natural balances designed to keep a species in tune with its environment. Upset that balance, and you get stress; stress leads to aggression; aggression to death; that seems to be the general patterns of events. As the earth fills up with people, so it does with animals they want to eat; and so does this factor of stress intensify. Amongst ourselves, we all recognise it: packed cities, rush-hour jams, snarled-up traffic; would-be escapers bumper-to-bumper on the roads; hip-to-hip on Sunday beaches; frustration and exasperation; mods and rockers, work-to-rule and go-slow protests, sense-less strikes, screaming teenage crowds.

As for the animals, the kinds man does not need are being exterminated, the kinds he does need packed in tighter and tighter; and so the likelihood of stress amongst them grows. To assume that they *must* all suffer, and all suffer equally, would be mistaken; some kinds, like birds, may suffer more than other kinds, like pigs, which are naturally more gregarious. If a susceptibility to stress should prove to be lodged in the genes, scientists may be able to dislodge it from our future domestic beasts, thus creating new strains of animal fitted for the new conditions mankind has imposed; one more stage in the long process of domestication that started with jungle fowls and wild cattle, mountain moufflons and roving swine.

It all needs careful watching meanwhile. To subject an animal to stress may be every bit as cruel as to starve or beat it; if this is so, ought not the same laws, indeed more stringent ones, apply? There is a need for our treatment of animals as living creatures to catch up with our techniques of treating them as sources of food. It is a fairly new idea that mental sickness in our own species merits our compassion as much as bodily disease. We have not yet got around to applying this idea to the animals. And yet it seems as if they, too, can be suffering acutely—even when they are warm, dry and well fed.

What turns into Miss T ?

It's a very odd thing,
As odd as can be,
That whatever Miss T eats
Turns into Miss T—

thus Walter de la Mare summed up, years ago, just about all that is known of human nutrition in the 'sixties. The more you look at it, the odder it becomes. With delicately refined techniques, scientists can analyse whatever Miss T eats not merely into its component proteins, fats, carbohydrates, minerals and vitamins, but into twenty amino-acids from which the proteins are built, into essential fatty acids which combine to make fat, into various vitamins which can be synthesised in laboratories, into esters and aldehydes and ketones and merceptans and sesquiterpenes and hundreds of other substances they can express as chemical formulae.

All these we eat, break down into their components and rebuild into bone, blood, nerve and muscle. Why, then, does a crumpet turn precisely into Miss T and into no one else? Why will the same carrot, if shared between them, turn into the Lord Chief Justice and into a donkey? Why does the same patch of grass, grazed by a sheep, a cow and a horse, become flesh that looks much the same and *is* pretty much the same chemically, but tastes quite different? Or identical grains of wheat become part of a pigeon's feather, a pig's trotter or a mathematician's brain?

Nor can anyone explain exactly what goes on in Miss T's insides. Are they really managing to get rid of all the

95

residues derived from the chemicals that killed the insects that attacked the barley that fed the pig that made the bacon Miss T had for breakfast? Are the anti-biotics that killed the bugs that infested the guts of the hen that laid the egg that shared the frying-pan with Miss T's bacon, working in some hidden way upon her own capacity to deal with infections? Does that same egg laid by a caged bird controlled by electricity and fed on compounded meal doctored with synthetics, lack something to be found in eggs laid by birds that walk freely in green fields, sunlight and open air, and search out natural foods? No one knows.

Miss T herself has strong views. Nothing tastes like it did. Those tailored little supermarket cuts of meat in trays and plastic wrappings may be convenient and tender, but they have no flavour; no wonder, when they come from animals that never saw daylight or a blade of grass. As for battery eggs, Miss T will not touch them— pale yolks, watery whites, thin shells.

How right, or how wrong, is Miss T? Is it true we are sacrificing quality to looks, nourishment to convenience, taste to tenderness? *Is* a battery egg inferior to a free-range one, and if so, how and why? What is quality in food, anyway? Can it be measured? Will all this food, intensively produced indoors, lack something that Miss T's metabolism needs?

To start with, part of the trouble lies with Miss T. She is over forty-five. Around this age, most people's taste-buds, lodged in their soft palates, begin to atrophy: slowly at first, sensitivity declines, and so she is quite right—nothing tastes as it did to her when she was young. You can prop up your sight and hearing with spectacles and deaf-aids, but for failing taste-buds there is no remedy.

Nor do scientists, with all their complex apparatus,

know exactly why, and how, cheese (let us say) tastes of cheese and not of soap, porridge or apples; let alone why it tastes not merely of cheese but of Stilton or Gruyère or Brie. Over thirty volatile components go towards the smell of roasting coffee, and one of these, called furfuryl mercaptan, may be chiefly responsible; but when all the analyses are done the question still remains open, writes a somewhat despairing chemist, "Why does coffee smell of *coffee?*" And not of leather, tripe or geraniums? No one knows.

I well remember, years ago in Aberdeen, sniffing from a small bottle of brown liquid an essence of kipper. Yet the kippery liquid had no connection with herrings. It had been extracted from sawdust. Food and its flavour can now be wholly divorced. In fact, chemists are approaching a point where almost any food *could* be made out of something else. We could have steaks made of cotton-wool tasting appetisingly of prime Scots beef, aromatic coffee made from coal, fresh cream from cabbage juice. "We may soon be presented," writes Professor John Yudkin, "with something that has the texture, taste, smell and cooking properties of beefsteak but contains no proteins, vitamins or any other nutrients. And we shall eat it because we like it." We could do this already with ice-cream, chocolates, biscuits, cakes and soft drinks. In a few years' time, sparrows will be pecking bottle-tops off milk that has never known a cow, but is derived from cabbage leaves, pea pods, stinging nettles and bracken.

Artificial milk is being made already, mainly from soya beans, and marketed for 1s. 5d. a pint. As production rises, costs will come down and soon, no doubt, meet the cost of the cow's version, which is going up. Not only that, the cow is less efficient than machinery at converting leafy matter; one of the inventors says his process does the job four times as well. And cows have the added disadvantage that they cannot be closed down over the weekend and during holidays.

This refusal to adopt a five-day, soon no doubt a four- and three-day week, may well price these antiquated, four-legged, herbage-processing machines right out of existence. Then all our milk will be more conveniently, cheaply and much more hygienically made in factories (mechanical, not animal). Technically, this could happen now. There is a commercial factory in Plymouth making protein-rich white powder out of groundnuts, and a research institute in Mysore working on similar lines. Millions of protein-deficient Afro-Asians will benefit, so it would be inhumane as well as futile to deplore the trend.

Technically, there is no reason why we should not eventually get *all* our protein direct from plants and by-pass animals, who merely break down the proteins into amino-acids and re-combine them in other forms. You could, nowadays, regard domestic animals as expensive, complicated and redundant devices to make the proteins appetising: elaborate packaging machines. Our digestive organs cannot convert into protein the leafier and more fibrous plants like grass, for which purpose the ruminant's multi-stomach system was evolved; machines can. Mr N. W. Pirie, F.R.S., of Rothamstead, the authority on all this, believes that the protein needs of all the multiplying millions east of Suez could be in part met by processes, essentially quite simple, that can extract protein from groundnuts, soya beans, oilseed residues, the leaves of bananas, sweet potatoes, sugar cane, peas, beans and many other crops, and water-weeds. It is not even unduly expensive; Mr Pirie reckons that equipment to turn out several hundred pounds of protein weekly can be set up for about £3,000, and run by a couple of men. In fact, the human race is now in a position to feed itself direct from plants and from laboratories, discarding everything on four legs and looking to the chemists to titivate the taste.

Palatability has been defined as that quality in food which makes people want to eat it—the bait. We are apt, quite wrongly, to link this with looks. A red, shiny apple looks nicer, and therefore (we think) ought to taste nicer, and to be better for us, than a green, blotchy one. We in Britain like our eggs brown-shelled. (Americans prefer them white.) Housewives treasure-hunting after brown-shelled eggs down the supermarket stacks is a familiar sight. "They won't pay extra for them, though," a manager sourly said.

An egg is brown only because the hen deposits a bit of pigment in the shell as it passes down her duct. Packaging, that is all. Nutritionally, there is no difference whatever between white- and brown-shelled eggs. Nor does the colour of the yolks reflect their food value. A pale yolk is pale simply because the diet of the hen has been low in xanthophyll, an ingredient of green leaves and yellow maize. A bit more grass meal in the diet will impart to her yolks a rich, golden, popular colour; whereas if, when on free range, she eats acorns, pennycress, shepherd's purse or too much lucerne or clover, the yolk will turn khaki, as repugnant to Miss T as yolks that are pallid.

So far, scientific experiments have not discerned any significant differences between the chemical composition of battery and of free-range eggs. In 1956 an Oxford nutritionist reported that the aortas of chicks hatched from eggs laid by battery hens gathered deposits of fat which were absent in the aortas of chicks derived from free-range birds. Among human beings, fatty deposits in the wall of the aorta can lead to heart disease. This depositing of fat in the chick's aorta was linked by the nutritionist, Dr Sinclair, to a deficiency in certain of the free fatty acids in the battery eggs which he examined, compared with those he analysed from free-range birds.

In 1961 several fellow-nutritionists published findings which disagreed with Dr Sinclair's. The battery eggs they analysed contained slightly *more* of the necessary fatty acids, not less, than the free-range sample. Suggesting that the determining factor was the time of year the eggs were laid, not the conditions under which the hens were kept, these scientists concluded: "Eggs produced under these two methods of husbandry are found to have closely similar fatty acid contents, provided that they are sampled at the same time during the laying period." Dr Sinclair retorted that if someone would give him a battery, some meal and an expensive bit of apparatus called a gas-liquid chromatograph, he would repeat the experiment; and the matter rests there.

It has also been suggested that battery eggs contain less vitamin A than free-range ones, and less of another vitamin called B_{12} which helps to prevent anaemia and to keep the nerve cells up to scratch. This has not been proved because it has never been investigated thoroughly enough to establish either proof or refutation acceptable to scientists. "It is dull work," was one explanation. "Long, laborious, routine analyses and probably very little to show at the end. The differences, if they exist at all, are tiny, and the fact is they do not matter in the normal British diet. We are so fully nourished these days we get all the vitamins we need without eggs."

We eat an average of less than one egg a day, and get from it less than eight per cent of our vitamin A, compared with twenty-seven per cent from margarine and butter, twenty-one per cent from meat, twenty per cent from vegetables, and ten per cent from milk. If eggs were cut out altogether, we would be all right for vitamin A, or could make it up from other sources. So even if battery eggs were found to have, say, ten per cent less vitamin A than free-range ones, our health would not be affected. As for the various vitamins lumped together under B, the most important probably is thiamine, and little more than three per cent of this we get from eggs; most of it comes from cereals (thirty-three per cent), and meat and vegetables (twenty-two per cent in each case). It is high in cereals largely because the law requires the millers to add thiamine to white flour, together with iron, nicotinic acid and calcium carbonate. (Wholemeal flour contains much less calcium than fortified white flour, but rather more thiamine and twice as much iron.) So generously enriched is white flour nowadays that rats will live and breed healthily on a diet of ninety-nine per cent white bread, which supplies six times as much of our thiamine as the brownest of eggs.

All this is the official line and critics say it is too complacent. How does anybody *know*? A lot of able scientists make careful analyses, but with tools which, intricate as they appear to a layman, are too blunt to reveal the inner secrets of living matter, or matter that was once alive. After all, if chemists do not know why coffee tastes of coffee or how quality can be defined, how can they pronounce upon the true nutritional value of an egg laid by a free-ranging hen, as against a synthesised chemical made in a laboratory and added to flour? There may be *more* of the B-group vitamins in white flour than in a dozen eggs, but are they the *same* vitamins? Scientists say they are, because synthetic vitamins are made of exactly the same atoms and molecules as natural ones, arranged in exactly the same way. Yet things remain to be revealed. There could even be an undiscovered vitamin, though this seems unlikely.

It is generally agreed that frozen broilers are lacking in flavour: therefore, lacking in nourishment. No connection, again. Flavour is mainly a matter of age. Youth is insipid; maturity equals flavour; ripeness is all. (Think of wine, plum puddings, cheese.) Four-year-old wethers are much tastier than lambs. The old-fashioned roasting bird was generally about twenty-six weeks old, the modern broiler is nine. We live on babies.

One enquiry did reveal certain differences between broiler meat, and that of chickens reared on free range. Frozen broilers lost more weight on cooking, had rather less breast meat, and retained in their flesh, after cooking, rather less of the fat and thiamine. Once again, the official line is that these differences are too small to matter. Less than half of one per cent of the thiamine in an average diet comes from poultry meat, as against over twenty-three per cent from enriched white bread.

Potatoes are another source of vitamins. To keep them white, some caterers steep them in sulphur dioxide which destroys part of their thiamine. Over half the thiamine succumbs to cooking, anyway. Nutritionists say all this does not matter as we have plenty of thiamine. Yes, but . . . if *everything* were to shed its vitamins as it gets steeped in anti-oxidants and acids, whitened and darkened, frozen and unfrozen, coloured and bleached, gassed and dehydrated, irradiated, sterilised, fortified and dyed as it progresses from the soil, or perhaps laboratory, to our stomachs, would not something get left out in the end?

No doubt it is true that, in our affluent and perhaps over-nourished country, most of us are eating all the vitamins, the proteins, the fat, the everything we need. We are certainly eating too much of some things, notably sugar. Nutritionally speaking, sugar is little more than potted energy. Of course we need energy, but less of it than we did, now that fewer of us are employed in hewing coal, wielding picks, humping sacks or scrubbing floors, and more in sitting still, and should therefore be eating foods with fewer calories—units of energy—and more vitamins and proteins. But actually we are mopping up many more calories because of our sweet tooth. Today we eat in a fortnight as much sugar as our ancestors, a couple of centuries back, ate in a year. Much of it goes to doll up cakes, biscuits, ice cream and various ready-mixes which persuade us to eat even *more* starchy foods high in calories, leaving insufficient room for nutritious comestibles.

As primitives, we lived on meat, roots and berries, and it was for these that our stomachs were designed. Then came the domestication of grass, which led to the growing of cereals, which enabled us to live—eventually—in cities on processed diets high in starchy matter. Nowadays, the richer we become as individuals, the more we tend to revert to the diet of the primitives by eating more beef and less bread. This would be fine if our sweet tooth did not undo us. Even the rich eat breakfast cereals, bread-and-butter, pastry and chocolate creams. They ought not to, since nearly all the rich are sedentary, and a diet overloaded with carbohydrates may well be a root cause of the increase in coronary thrombosis. Bursting with calories, the rich rot their children's teeth and contract heart diseases that are on the increase and have become the biggest killers in the Western world.

The Americans are being rather more sensible. As a nation, they eat less today (1,455 pounds a head a year) than in 1909 (1,616 pounds). In part, this is due to a higher proportion of children in the population. But also they have cut down more than we have on cereals and potatoes, stepped up meat, fruit, fish and vegetables, and eat on average fewer calories than we do, though still more than they need. (Consumption of TV dinners and frozen pies has gone up fifteen times in the last decade; atomic energy is being used to preserve food without canning or freezing; alcohol consumption per head, believe it or not, has gone down.)

The guardians of our health and diet do agree that a whole lot more investigation is needed. An institute is being planned in Bristol for meat research, and one in Norwich for studying other kinds of food. In years to come—we are very slow movers—researchers may advance some answers to such questions as to what quality in food consists of, and how it makes us what we are. Of how and why

> *Porridge and apples*
> *Mince, muffins and mutton,*
> *Jam, junket, jumbles—*

it does not matter what; the moment

> *They're out of her plate,*
> *Though shared by Miss Butcher*
> *And sour Mr Bate,*
>
> *Tiny and cheerful*
> *As neat as can be—*
> *Whatever Miss T eats*
> *Turns into Miss T.*

World War

INSECTS, fungi, micro-organisms and weeds—pests, in our estimation—that prey upon our crops and domestic animals are calculated every year to destroy, between them, enough of the world's food to sustain 1,000 million people, which is about the number at present underfed or actually hungry. In Britain alone, they wipe out about seventeen per cent of all our crops and set us back between £150 and £200 million a year in crop and livestock losses, plus the cost of trying to keep them down.

No crop or beast is free of damage from pests of some kind, generally of several kinds; and, as farming methods intensify, so do losses. Blight, rot, eelworms, viruses and insects between them have been estimated to spoil, on average, about 14·5 per cent of Britain's potato crop,[1] which works out at an annual toll of about twenty-eight hundredweights from every acre of potatoes in these islands. About seven per cent of our sugar beet is destroyed, an average loss of one ton an acre. At a time when output per acre may determine the grower's economic survival, and when the number of the world's hungry people increases year by year, we cannot afford to forego any methods science can devise to combat these predators, provided they do not damage humans as well as pests on a serious scale.

[1] See George Ordish, *Untaken Harvest*. Over the past five years the potato crop has averaged just under six million tons grown on about 650,000 acres. Since mechanical harvesting has become almost universal, more potatoes are rejected for human consumption by reason of mechanical damage than for damage by disease.

Chemical pesticides have recently come under a cloud in public esteem. They poison plants and animals, so why should they not poison humans too? Some do, if they are not properly handled. So-called organic farmers (the muck-and-magic men) go to the length of believing the use of such chemicals to be an error for which we shall pay by poisoning ourselves in subtle, long-term ways we cannot yet recognise, but which in the end will destroy our health and even our society. They refuse, themselves, to use such chemicals, and would like to see them all banned. Such last-ditchers are the zealots of our world, battling for a theory basically religious, in the sense that it is mystical. Right or wrong, they are un-likely to halt, let alone reverse, the trend towards a con-tinued, and increasing, use on the land of chemicals which poison those plants and animals we do not want around.

How well founded are these fears? Very few people have actually been killed by chemical sprays, only a small handful of men who have been careless about applying them. That is not the problem. The fear is that the poisons are getting into animals and plants, and through them into us, to harm us in ways we do not yet understand: not directly perhaps, or even immediately, but mysteriously, slowly and in a cumulative way. "Con-tamination of the habitat"—a sinister phrase. Is the world being contaminated? If so, how, and what can be done?

Perhaps the first thing to be clear about is that there are, very broadly speaking, two kinds of chemical in-volved: those that kill insects and fungi, and those that kill plants. These are, respectively, insecticides and herbicides, all classed together as pesticides. These two classes of chemical have very different properties and natures. The first aim to kill our fellow-creatures in the more humble categories of the animal world, and so are potentially more dangerous to humans. One-fifth of the chemicals used today in this country on the land are directed against insects and fungi, four-fifths against plants.

In order to kill living creatures, the poison must persist for a certain length of time. Poisons that persist in plants or soils accumulate; that is where the trouble lies. The most persistent, and therefore the most effective, belong to classes called the organo-phosphates and the organo-chlorines. These came into use only after World War II, as a result of research into aspects of chemical warfare. Before that, chemicals used for spraying were made from natural elements combined in various ways together; these post-war chemicals are synthesised in laboratories by rearranging atoms and molecules. DDT, for instance, an organo-chlorine (short for diclorodiphenyl-trichloro-ethane), was synthesised by a Swiss firm in 1942. About the same time a German, Dr Schrader, completed his discovery of the first synthetic organo-phosphate compounds.

After the war, derivatives considerably more lethal than DDT emerged from the laboratories: dieldrin (five times as toxic as DDT) and aldrin, heptachlor and parathion, BHC, DNOC (killer of poppies) and many others; today about 750 different kinds of pesticide are on sale, and each year their number rises. Marketed by a dynamic and powerful industry to whom they are a gold mine, their use has quickly spread throughout the world.

It is these organo-chlorines and organo-phosphates that were Rachel Carson's main target in *Silent Spring*. Few books have had more impact on American public opinion, indeed on legislation; as a result, dieldrin, aldrin and heptachlor were outlawed in the United States.

"For the first time in the history of the world," Rachel Carson wrote, "every human being is subjected to contact with dangerous chemicals from the moment of conception until death"; a death sometimes, in her view, hastened by these chemicals, some of which she believed to possess the property of affecting the behaviour of the human body's cell structure in such ways as to trigger off forms of cancer. The public alarm caused by this powerfully presented thesis led the late President Kennedy to appoint a scientific committee to examine the question in detail.

The average American, this committee found, is walking around with twelve parts per million (about 100-200 mg) of DDT residues secreted in his tissues, mainly in his fat and liver. This rises to seventeen parts per million (p.p.m.) amongst farm workers, and up to 648 p.p.m. among workers in factories making insecticides. No one can exactly define the lethal concentration of such residues. If very few people have actually been poisoned, it is difficult to know just what is going on because "the symptoms of pesticide toxicity are little different from those of many common illnesses".

Once, after a terrible flood, a sympathiser hit upon the happy phrase: "The United States is great even in her disasters." This is certainly true of disasters caused by chemical sprays, for the reason that such chemicals are used on a scale unknown in any other country. Instead of a field or two here and there, North Americans spray millions of acres. Rachel Carson instances the spraying of several million acres of forest in New Brunswick against spruce budworm. The aerial application of as little as half a pound of DDT to the acre killed the budworm, and also nearly all the salmon in the rivers; a whole year's spawning was wiped out.

Since Rachel Carson's tragic death, an even greater

disaster has occurred. In November, 1963, in the Mississippi river basin, more than five million fish expired, plus vast numbers of duck, full of DDT residues. The following March, a report by Federal authorities laid the blame on the spraying of sugar cane, cotton and maize. Residues had drained into the Mississippi and its tributaries, and poisoned the fish and birds.

Whether or not harm could come to humans from eating the contaminated fish was said to be a matter for investigation. In the spring of 1964 the local newspaper reported: "Fish have died here by the million: shad and mullet, bass, trout, catfish and gar, the smallest to the largest, surfacing, swimming, drifting and dying"; white cranes "died by countless thousands" and a reporter counted only five crows where there had once been millions.

In our own island, matters have proceeded in a more decorous and restrained style. As long ago as 1952, dead birds and rabbits picked up in the Eastern countries were found to have perished from an organo-phosphate used against an aphis pest of brussels sprouts. From 1959 onwards, reports came in, mainly from East Anglia, of game birds dying of a mysterious ailment. Then dead foxes were found. At first, an epidemic was suspected. Then the cause was traced to the organo-chlorine heptachlor mixed into compounds used to dress the seed of spring wheat against bulb-fly. The birds ate the dressed wheat and died; the foxes ate the dead birds and *they* died. Eventually this was overcome by a voluntary agreement on everyone's part not to dress spring wheat with heptachlor, but only winter wheat, which seems not to matter to the birds.

This was not the end of the story. Ornithologists drew attention to a reduction in the numbers of birds of prey. For this there were many reasons, among them an increasing sterility. Eggs did not hatch, and when examined were discovered to contain residues of DDT and other organo-chlorines. This re-kindled public alarm, as any threat to British bird life is bound to do. Other causes for disquiet arose. In June, 1963, a committee, by no means the first on this topic, was appointed under the chairmanship of Sir James Cook, F.R.S., Vice-Chancellor of the University of Exeter, to "review the risks arising from the use of chlorinated hydrocarbon pesticides", especially aldrin, dieldrin and heptachlor, and recommend what was to be done.[1]

This committee turned in a report that soothed rather than alarmed. True, its scientific panel found residues of the DDT group in butter, milk, mutton, beef fat and potatoes, but in small quantities, not more than an average of two parts per million, compared with seventeen p.p.m. in the United States. Such small traces can do no harm to anyone, it seems; in the opinion of Sir Harold Sanders, until lately Chief Scientific Advisor to the Ministry of Agriculture, Food and Fisheries, "for all we know, they may be doing us good". Although "undesirably high residues" might, on occasion, occur in sheep slaughtered within a month or two of being dipped in dieldrin compounds, their meat was "unlikely to contribute appreciably to the diet throughout the whole year".

Nevertheless, the committee struck a note of caution. Domestic animals *can* be poisoned by too much DDT, causing "widespread tremors and disorganised muscular activity"; people engaged in malaria eradication over-

[1] Report by the Advisory Committee on Poisonous Substances Used in Agriculture and Food Storage. H.M.S.O., February, 1964. Previous committees reported in 1951 (risks to workers), 1953 (residues in foods) and 1955 (risks to wild life). There is also a standing committee of the Agricultural Research Council under Professor A. C. Frazer.

seas *have* suffered from "serious or repeated convulsions"; large doses of dieldrin and aldrin *do* injure the livers of laboratory mice; rats on diets containing ten p.p.m. of DDT store less vitamin A in their livers than normal rats; in Washington, investigators described DDT, aldrin and dieldrin as having a "weak carcinogenic" (cancer inducing) or "slight tumorigenic" potential. And while there is at present "no scientific evidence that DDT does any injury while it is in the fat", it is also the case that "new information may emerge at any time". The committee reported that "Small accumulations and residues in human bodies, human food, wild birds, fish, soil and some of the creatures which live in it, and in water, suggest a widespread contamination of living things and their environment. . . . The root cause of this contamination is the unusual persistence of some of these pesticides, which retain their biologically active form over quite long periods. When they have done their job of controlling particular pests or diseases, they do not degrade into harmless substances as many other pesticides do, but retain their toxic properties and find their way into situations where they accumulate, are unwelcome and may, in sufficient concentration, do harm."

As to what is to be done, the contamination of the environment should be "contained" rather than avoided; Sir James Cook's committee saw no reason to panic and condemn all these chemicals. Modern farming, in fact, could not carry on without them.

As to the suspect pair dieldrin and aldrin, their use in sheep-dips, fertilisers and general farm and garden sprays "should cease as soon as this can be arranged"; and a subsequent Ministerial statement led people to believe that by the end of 1965 they would be withdrawn from use except in certain specified cases, such as seed-dressings for winter wheat and sugar beet, and against wireworm in potatoes and narcissus bulb fly. The rest of the organo-chlorines and phosphates were to carry on as before.

What with one thing and another, it has not yet been possible to arrange that the fairly widespread use of dieldrin and aldrin should cease in 1965. On the contrary, several more specific uses have been approved, such as to help control leather-jackets in barley, hop-root weevil, strawberry-seed beetle and onion fly. The outcome seems, in the words of the public relations officer of the firm that makes them, to be: "neither dieldrin nor aldrin will be withdrawn from sale to commercial users, though the recommendations on the label will be considerably reduced. It is true that farmers and growers could ignore the recommendations and use them as they have done in the past. . . ." But they will not do anything so dastardly because, as we all know, farmers and growers are "responsible members of the community".

They will face temptations, especially if they keep sheep. A single application of a dieldrin dip or spray protects a sheep against blowfly for the whole summer. A farmer who uses any other preparation must dip or spray his sheep at least twice, having perhaps to drive them off the hills in August when he is busy harvesting; and everyone is short of shepherds nowadays. Some of the sheep might have to go without their second treatment, and then the fly would "strike" and maggots hatch and eat away their living flesh, causing horrible festering wounds. So at present, unless and until the chemical industry can invent a new compound as effective as dieldrin but not as harmful, there seems to be a choice between sheep getting eaten alive by maggots on the one hand and fish being poisoned and birds made infertile by residues on the other. In theory, no more dieldrin is to be used in sheep dips from the end of 1965, but in practice, so long as it is on sale, everyone will be surprised if a good many farmers, however responsible they are to the community, do not continue to rely on it. Farmers feel responsible also to their sheep, after all.

As for DDT, life without it would now scarcely seem to be liveable, so widely is it used. But the insects are fighting back by developing resistant strains. Just as certain strains of bacteria now resist certain antibiotics, so have strains of insect appeared whose nervous systems no longer succumb to the organo-chlorine poisons. Already strains of about 135 species of insect or tick have emerged with the genetical ability to ignore the pesticides that formerly destroyed them.

Especially in the tropics, this is causing serious alarm. A capsid bug which preys on cocoa trees throughout West Africa has, hitherto, been satisfactorily controlled by spraying with BHC. In 1961 resistant strains appeared and now the salvation of the cocoa crop, the mainstay of Ghana and parts of Nigeria, from capsid attack is a major problem of the industry. In Britain, the German cockroach has developed resistance to dieldrin, but the Oriental cockroach so far has not. Some kinds of Australian blowfly have made the same adaptation. The cabbage-root fly has got on top of aldrin and the red spider mite, a glasshouse pest, can now survive applications of some of the organo-phosphates. The Colorado beetle, the codling moth and several cattle ticks have learnt to cope with DDT, and the common housefly shows disturbing signs of doing the same.

"Unless some method can be found to overcome this matter of resistant strains," said a pesticide authority, "the prospect is bleak. At present, the only way that we can deal with them is to keep ringing the changes; accustom the insects to one chemical and then bash them with another; keep several weapons in the armoury. That is expensive, and not very satisfactory. This is the biggest difficulty the chemical industry is faced with."

Since 1954, a scheme of voluntary notification has been in operation. It works as follows. Every firm proposing to market a new pesticide notifies the Ministry of Agriculture, Food and Fisheries, who pass the application on to one of three laboratories dealing respectively with plant pathology, stored products and veterinary medicine. The information supplied by the manufacturer must be full and detailed, not only about the chemical nature of the new compound but also about tests made on animals, birds and fish, and assessments of the residues in food crops, possible carcinogenic effects, and other matters.

The Government laboratory concerned takes a close look at the compound and either approves it, or, if there is any doubt, passes it to the Advisory Committee on Poisonous Substances Used in Agriculture and Food Storage. This body, in turn, refers it to a scientific subcommittee of seventeen independent experts who give it a going-over, and make recommendations to their parent body, which is fully stocked with high-powered scientists, pundits and civil servants, but no manufacturers. If these authorities are not fully satisfied, they refer the product back to its manufacturers for modifications or further tests. Products which pass through all these hoops get a clearance certificate from the Ministry plus a set of recommendations for safe use. Without this certificate, nothing must be marketed.

Humans are fallible, even Fellows of the Royal Society and men from the Ministry; mistakes can be made and the jigsaw of knowledge is very far from complete. However many tests are made in the laboratory, no one can foretell for certain what will happen when a chemical is spread on the land and used on animals. Nor do people always follow the directions on the label. Fish and birds have been killed as a result of empty containers being chucked into streams and ditches. Sprays have been put on too strong, or when there is a wind that blows them into the wrong places to damage hedges and fruit trees. Lots of things can go wrong, and some do. But it is more often due to not doing what auntie says, or to auntie's own ignorance, than to her reckless disregard of consequences.

And then, sometimes aunties disagree. There are chemicals banned in the United States on sale here, and vice versa; our watchdogs have rejected a potato spray used in Holland; aldrin and dieldrin were banned in New Zealand long before we got around to it here. When it comes to food "additives", things are even more confused; we allow thirty kinds of dye for colouring ices, cakes, sweets and biscuits, most of which the Americans prohibit; they allow fifteen of which we ban nine; apart from these, anything non-toxic may be added to our foods unless it is specifically prohibited, whereas since 1959 the West Germans have banned virtually all food additives—preservatives, antioxidants, emulsifiers, stabilisers, sweeteners, tenderizers, antibiotics, a whole Pandora's box of chemicals. Everyone is groping in the dark. We must take comfort from the fact that at least they do grope, and do not turn their backs on the whole thing.

Most people now agree that tests should be longer and fuller. The chemical industry is highly competitive, and pressure very strong to move anything new on to the market before the rival backroom boys across the way get on to it. This pressure has forced new products into use before they should have been. More research is needed; in particular, one would suppose, into the possible long-term effects of many of these substances on the fundamental structure of the human body: on the genes, and on the life and death of cells.

Ever reaping Something New

THE farmer's central object is to control the plants which grow on his land. If you leave the land alone, it will soon achieve what scientists call an ecological climax: it will grow the kinds of plant it wants to, not the kind that humans want. In Britain, woodland is the natural climax; left to itself, most of the country, apart from such areas as chalk downs, Eastern county brecks and marshes, and high hill land, would revert to the woods we have been cutting down ever since the Saxons got busy with their wooden ploughs.

In growing cereals or, for that matter, modern and high-yielding grasses and clovers, farmers fight a constant battle against what they call weeds. Weeds are simply plants the farmer or gardener does not want in any given spot. If they are in the wrong place and at the wrong time, he has to destroy them. This he can do either with the hoe, which kills them outright, or with the plough, which buries them under the soil and stifles them. The first aim of ploughing is to bury, and so if possible to kill, the weeds.

As labour costs rise so ploughing, however mechanised, gets more and more expensive. The next thing to be mechanised may be the man on the tractor, who will become as obsolete as the man who trudged behind the horse if the control of tractors by radio, now in its experimental stage, succeeds. The future ploughman, then, will sit in his control-room manipulating switches and twiddling dials, while the obedient manless tractor draws its mounted plough across the fields. This will not be cheap, but it will enable one man to drive, say, half a dozen tractors simultaneously. Another line of approach is to do away with ploughing altogether, and substitute the chemical spray.

Plants, like animals, regulate their growth by means of hormones. Natural hormones carry to the various parts of the plant instructions which cause its cells to multiply in a normal manner. Synthetic hormones may carry false instructions; these the plant obeys, and grows in a distorted and lop-sided fashion. The whole growth process then goes haywire; leaves shrivel and curl, stems twist and writhe, the plant withers. When a synthetic hormone spray inadvertently got on to some potatoes, the shoots grew inwards. A pansy grower whose prize blooms grew deformed and double-headed discovered that a mishap in a chemical factory half a mile away had wafted a hormone powder through the air. Synthetic hormone weed-killers have been developed by the chemical industry since 1942, when the original discovery was made by Dr W. G. Templeton at Jealott's Hill in Berkshire. They caught on quickly all over the world. In Britain alone, five million acres out of (roughly) seven million acres of cereal crops are now sprayed every year, not to mention orchards, market-gardens, roadside verges and pastures.

Chemical weed control in pastures, however, is in its infancy, and now chemists have made a discovery they think may prove almost as revolutionary as the earlier synthesis of plant hormones. It is a chemical called paraquat ($1, 1'$-dimethul-4, 4-bipyridyline as the dichloride salt, if you like formulae) which blasts everything that is green and growing, and leaves a wake of scorched earth. Run a sprayer over a pasture, and all the grass is killed without the trouble and expense of turning it under with a plough and then working down a seedbed with harrows and rolls. One operation and the job is done; and you can plant your seed the same day, the same hour even; paraquat does not linger. Into the rural museum with the plough, alongside scythe and flail and smock. Chemistry takes over.

This new spray is in use already on hills too steep and awkward to plough; after it has done its work, superior grasses can replace coarse, un-nutritious mountain pastures. The weight of lamb-meat produced off such pastures has been stepped up, in one spectacular instance in Wales, by nine times. Overseas, potentialities are even greater. Ever since the subjects of the Roman Empire turned the granary of North Africa into a desert, people have been mining soil, cutting down forests, diminishing springs and generally plundering their planet. If they use chemicals instead of ploughs, so say the chemists, they need not any longer leave their land bare of cover for sun and wind to ravage and erode. "For the first time in history, we can avoid creating deserts and dust-bowls, and do away with soil erosion." It is a rosy vision. Snags? One will certainly be to convince the under-developed peoples, who during the brief but disturbing span of colonialism were constantly exhorted to abandon hoes for ploughs, now to abandon ploughs for sprayers.

Paraquat persists in the ground only a matter of minutes. The chemists also claim that, unlike compounds used to kill insects and fungi, synthetic plant hormones do not linger in the soil when their job is done. Expiring with the plants they destroy, they have no ill-effects on plants which come after. At least, that was the theory until an odd event occurred in 1963. In several places, crops of glasshouse cucumbers and tomatoes started to go wrong. Their leaves began to twist and curl, yields fell off, and some of the tomatoes grew elongated instead of round. It was just as if they had been treated with a hormone weed-killer. But no such chemical had been applied. Eventually the trouble was traced to residues in the straw of cereals that had been sprayed the previous year with a herbicide called 2,3,6-TBA. This chemical was present in the straw in quantities so small that chemical tests had failed to detect them; but tomatoes and cucumbers had done so, and it destroyed them.

Since then, the comfortable belief that hormone weed-killers do not persist in the soil has begun to sag a little, if it has not actually collapsed. So far, no instances have come to light, or been proved experimentally, where this persistence has lasted much above a year, but that it may last as long as that now seems established. Researchers in New Zealand found that normal crops of lettuces and turnips could not be grown for twelve to fifteen months after 2,3,6-TBA had been used. Traces of the common hormone weedkillers 2,4-D and MCPA have been recovered ninety days after application. So caution now prevails; one authority, Dr T. J. Sheets, has concluded that "carry-over from one year to the next can be expected under some conditions", even if the possibilities of "massive accumulation seem rather remote".

If these synthetic hormone weedkillers turn out, as the organo-chlorines did, to be more persistent than the chemists first believed, what effect, if any, will they have upon the soil bacteria and soil animals on whose activities all soil fertility ultimately depends? As yet, this question has scarcely been investigated; practice, once again, has pushed ahead of knowledge; we know not what we do. The effects may, of course, turn out to be negligible. There is no evidence, as yet, that any harm has been done. The quantities of alien chemicals that can possibly accumulate from the use of all these herbicides is so tiny that they must take years to build up to a level likely to disturb the balance of the soil. Nevertheless, plants, as we have seen, and therefore bacteria (which belong to the plant order), can be much more sensitive to tiny traces of synthetic drugs than any scientific apparatus hitherto invented. We are dabbling in the unknown and the conjectural—as, of course, mankind has always done, and no doubt always will do; safety first, that unheroic maxim, has never been our guiding light.

All forms of chemical spray are condemned with passion and persistence by the muck-and-magic, "organic" school banded together in the Soil Association, who crusade against the destruction, as they believe, of soil fertility by poisonous, synthetic chemicals. In their view soil fertility can be husbanded and enhanced only through the natural cycle of growth, maturity, decay and regeneration; the soil fauna, from earthworms to bacteria, working with sunlight, air and moisture, alone can sustain the plants which in turn sustain the animals. This is an immemorial, fundamental process which all these synthetic compounds, behaving in a manner we fail to understand, can only distort and destroy, bringing ultimate disaster to mankind. "You cannot maintain life with non-life," these believers say.

A bunch of cranks, or a circle of prophets? Their essential point, as I understand it, is that differences between the organic and the non-organic are not just differences of degree, but of kind. Life, which eludes definition, is not just a stage in chemistry; it is a mystery, something sacred that we play about with at our peril. Life cannot be mocked, and synthesis is mockery. Basically, theirs is a religious belief, and, like all faiths, cannot be treated logically; it operates on a different wavelength. Naturally this annoys the scientists, many of whom hold with equal conviction the belief that everything, including the property of life, can ultimately be understood in terms of matter, even if that goal lies a long way ahead.

Organic farmers, however, are by no means all starry-eyed theorists turning compost heaps under a waxing moon. Some are practical men who run their farms as businesses and make them pay. They concede that this is more difficult than to rely on chemical fertilisers to boost the yields of crops, chemical sprays to keep down weeds, and chemical drugs to treat animal diseases. It is more difficult mainly because it takes more time and trouble, and this in turn calls for more man-hours, and man-hours grow more and more expensive. But it can be done, they say.

What is more, they say it *must* be done or we, the human race, will be undone. What they call for is the ecological approach—treating men, animals, plants, the soil and the entire habitat as one whole, living process, the life-cycle; and considering always the relationship, the balance, between them. We ignore this balance, this harmony, they say, at our peril. We *are* ignoring it, and perils threaten us. Although our overall health as a nation has never been so good, and there is certainly nothing wrong—perhaps too little?—with our collective reproductive system, the so-called "diseases of civilisation" are on the increase. These include cancer in its various forms, notably leukaemia; thrombosis, arteriosclerosis, arthritis, ulcers, kidney diseases; above all, nervous and mental illnesses, which now afflict nearly half the patients under treatment in our affluent but fretful society. All these are getting worse, not better. Things are not as right as, on the surface, they appear to be.

Unbelievers have their answers; there are more of us, and so we are bound to have more diseases; some of these are probably promoted by urban conditions and the stress of our society, not by anything wrong with our food; of course there is a lot more to be discovered, but the fact remains that we *are* healthier than ever before, and living much longer. (Too long?) Without chemical sprays and fertilisers, a great many more people would have emptier bellies and come earlier to the grave. It is one of those arguments that can go on forever, with neither side ever likely to give way.

The high prophet of the organic farmers was Sir Albert Howard, whose work in India on the making of compost laid the foundations of the faith about thirty years ago. His followers are to be found all over the world. In Switzerland, for instance, six peasants got together immediately after World War II to collect refuse in wheelbarrows from greengrocers' shops and markets, wheel it to their smallholdings and turn it into compost, and so back into vegetables again. ("And as a cabbage, kings re-enter Rome.") Today, those six peasants have multiplied, almost like soil bacteria, into four hundred groups of farmers who not only replenish their soil with organic matter instead of with inorganic fertilisers, but claim that they save money this way, and so make better profits. And one of the largest chain stores in Switzerland annually makes contracts with them, at competitive prices, for half a million pounds' worth of produce which Swiss consumers are apparently delighted to buy. Everything these organic farmers can produce is sold before it is grown, and marketed through a co-operative which collects and grades it, allocates a quota to each group, and runs its own advisory service and training school. Most of the members have abandoned composting as too expensive, and replaced it by a technique of mulching and green manuring under irrigation—organic still (they call it *biologique*) with no fertilisers.

In Britain, the Soil Association has developed on different lines: not as a co-operative to market organically produced crops, but as a centre of investigation. Twenty-five years ago its members started on a farm at Haughley, in Suffolk, to study "the nutritional effects on successive generations of farm animals of food grown from successive generations of crops". Their intention was to find out, through a series of controlled experiments scientifically directed and planned, whether differences exist that can be measured and assessed, in terms of the health and productiveness of animals, between crops that are grown with sprays and fertilisers, and crops that are grown without.

So, at Haughley, there are three systems of husbandry. Crops on the Stockless section are fertilised and sprayed with chemicals. The Mixed section has cows as well as crops, plus sheep and poultry, and also uses fertilisers and sprays. On the Organic section, these chemicals are banned. The livestock on this and on the Mixed sections are exactly matched, so far as this is possible, in numbers, ages, types and breeds, and on both sections are supported, except for a little seaweed and fishmeal, by crops grown on the land.

Fertilisers, undoubtedly, jack up yields. But crops on the Organic section have proved more resistant to disease. And the cows on this section have, over the years, kept healthier, lived longer, experienced less breeding trouble and proved more efficient at converting their food into milk, than those on the Mixed section. The pastures on the Organic section seldom look as good. Sometimes they are grazed almost bare, and make a poor showing beside the Mixed section's tall, green, juicy grasses on leys generously treated with nitrogenous fertilisers. Oddly enough, though, cows which graze the barer pastures, while they get less bulk, yield more milk: since 1956, about eight or nine per cent more than cows on the Mixed section.

"We do not know why, or why the cows thrive better, but they do," I was told. "These cows also keep up their milk yields better later in life. On our Organic pastures there are deep-rooted herbs, and plants normally considered to be weeds; these may have something to do with it, though they cannot be the whole answer. The other day we took an Australian round. He was not much interested until I mentioned that our Guernseys seemed to prefer the eaten-down, bare-looking paddocks to the lusher ones. 'I have a paddock like that at home and my cattle always make for it instead of for the leys,' he said. Yet our leys produce a greater weight of leafier grasses which are richer in protein. The heaviest yielding pastures on our Organic section, in terms of milk, are those which have been longest without fertilisers, some nearly thirty-five years. We don't know why. We believe there is an unknown factor and we want to find out what it is."

Three hundred miles to the west, at the Welsh Plant Breeding Station near Aberystwyth, experiments on sheep have seemed to pick up the theme of those at Haughley. The researchers penned two lots of sheep on two plots. On one, the sheep grazed normally, returning their dung and urine to the soil. On the other plot, the sheep's wastes were collected in containers strapped to their bodies, analysed, and an exact chemical equivalent returned to their plot in the form of inorganic fertilisers. Differences between the behaviour of plants growing on the two plots soon began to appear. White clover growing on the plot that received inorganic fertiliser fell off, but increased on the plot the sheep themselves had manured. While the total yield of herbage remained about the same, the composition of the sward changed in the direction of suppressing the protein-rich clover, whose root nodules possess the power to extract nitrogen from the air and fix it in a form digestible to animals. The researchers commented: "We do not know what it is that appears to be present in the sheep's dung and urine, but lacking in the fertiliser, that encourages clover, nor do we know why some species of plant are more sensitive to this than others are."

The air is our sole source of nitrogen, and nitrogen the source of protein in our bodies. It is extracted for our use either by chemical factories, where it is made into inorganic fertilisers, or by bacteria living on the roots of legumes, notably certain clovers, which store the nitrogen in their tissues. Grazing animals eat the plants and turn the nitrogen into protein. Thus is the life-cycle continually replenished. Chemically speaking, nitrogen is just nitrogen, an element, no different whether it reaches the plant by way of a fertiliser factory in Liverpool[1] or a nodule on the root of a white clover plant. And yet, for reasons not yet unravelled, there seems to be a difference in the way some plants respond.

British farmers look mainly to factories for the nitrogen needed by their crops and pastures, and are applying to their grassland three times as much inorganic nitrogen as they were in 1952. Dutch farmers apply even more, and probably achieve the highest yields of pasture in the world. On the other hand New Zealand farmers, blessed by mild winters and ample sunshine, rely on clovers to

[1] At the largest group of chemical factories in Europe, covering over two and a half square miles near Frankfurt, in a laboratory called U508, a specially designed desk-sized computer now controls the processes which synthesise a number of compounds, including nitrogenous fertilisers. Besides handling the technical and chemical complexities of its task, it takes into account the constant price fluctuations of eight raw materials and seven end-products involved in the process. Apart from the prices, to which they are indifferent, all this can be done by bacteria in nodules on a root of clover, and by the leaves of grass which turn sunlight, air and water into chlorophyll.

do the job. Carcases of clover-fed lambs have been compared with carcases of lambs fed on grass liberally fertilised with inorganic nitrogen. Otherwise the lambs were alike in all respects—breed, age, sex and date of slaughter. In the same period, the clover-eaters put on twenty-five per cent more weight, and put the meat on more evenly.

Why? As yet, no one knows the answer. Nitrogen is unpredictable. Could the different methods by which it was extracted from the air, by living bacteria and inanimate machines respectively, somehow have affected the lambs' digestive systems, or the way in which they turned it into protein, or the kind of protein they formed? Was the protein in the clover somehow more digestible than the protein in the grass? As yet, the biochemists have no answer. Nitrogen, they repeat, is just nitrogen; one of the fundamental elements of which the universe and all that it contains is built. It cannot vary, and nor can the proteins into which it is combined, with other elements, by all living things. There is a formula and all formulae, by definition, stay the same.

The undiscovered world, retort the anti-chemists, is much too wide to allow of dogmatism. In the book of life there are no full-stops. So let scientists be more humble, and admit how little they still know about the soil, the plants that grow in it, the animals that eat the plants and we who eat both: about the chain of being, the ecosystem in which we have a place, yet not perhaps that central hub, that imperial core, we believe ourselves to occupy.

Meanwhile, chemistry works. On those who abhor chemical pesticides rests the onus to suggest alternatives. We cannot just let the weeds and insects rip, and most of the traditional methods of control have priced themselves out of the market in the technologically advanced parts of the world.

To the goal of pest control there exist what have been described as "circuitous routes"—long cuts. One of these is to breed plants which have a built-in resistance to a particular disease. To do this, you must first find plants growing in a natural state which possess an immunity they can pass on to their offspring through their genes.

Genes are a sort of bank on which the plant breeders draw, and if the right gene is not in the bank they cannot, so far, put it there. Fortunately the bank is fabulously rich in genes. For instance, plant breeders have recently found a barley plant resistant to the damage done to most barley plants by DDT, a contingency one would scarcely have expected the world of plants to have foreseen. "Everything exists in nature," a geneticist affirmed. An important part of modern plant breeding is to comb the world for specimens of the variety of plant you are concerned with, whether a wheat or potato, a cabbage or cucumber or rose. Then you grow them all under controlled conditions, see how each one reacts to any given disease, and ultimately cross those which display resistance with varieties possessing other virtues, such as high yields.

Hitherto the geneticist's main and remarkable achievement, aided of course by fertilisers and sprays, has been to increase the yields of many crops twofold, threefold, fourfold or even more. There is scarcely one of real importance that has not been thus improved in the last half-century, and the process continues all the time. Breeding for resistance to disease is much more difficult. Fewer genes appear to carry the necessary properties, which in any case are little understood; the genes that do so are less reliable, and all sorts of complications enter in. Nevertheless, most of the cereals grown today have had bred into them some measure of resistance to diseases caused by fungi such as rust, smut and bunt. There are strains of cotton that resist insect predators, sugars and tomatoes that stand up to harmful viruses, potatoes that (with luck) resist blight. A classic example occurred when an insect called *Phylloxera*, introduced from North America, spread havoc and disaster in the vineyards of France. Resistant rootstocks were brought over to replace the susceptible European rootstocks, and the situation was redeemed.

This was not the work, however, of geneticists, but of viticulturalists who simply made use of the natural resistance of existing plant material. The geneticist goes farther, and blends the genes to create new strains of plant. All Proctor barley, of which in 1964 we grew three million acres in Britain, came from a single plant. Now it is having tolerance to yellow-dwarf virus, derived from a single gene, bred into it by means of a continuous back-cross programme. The Welsh Plant Breeding Station at Aberystwyth recently bred a variety of oat called Manod, derived from strains collected from Algeria, Argentine, the United States, Sweden and Scotland, which resists three diseases: mildew, crown rust and stem eelworm. This is the first time a treble immunity has been bred into a cereal, and the project took thirty-nine years to complete. This is longer than usual; most pedigree breeding programmes take between fifteen and twenty years, and some can be compressed into about ten.

The average time taken to get a new synthetic chemical from laboratory to field is five years. To kill the pest with poisons, therefore, is a lot quicker, easier and cheaper, and often more reliable, than to breed resistant plant varieties. Nevertheless, the plant breeder may have a better answer than the chemist in the long run. He adds something to nature's bank instead of depleting it; creates, not kills. No other creature is injured, nothing is destroyed. "Chemicals should be used as a walking stick, not as a crutch," said a geneticist. "We should be well advised to put more of our effort into plant breeding, and resign ourselves to waiting rather longer for results."

But we are in a hurry. Besides, you can seldom make money out of plant breeding, whereas chemicals are very paying indeed. The result is that chemicals are made by large, efficient firms, and most plant breeding is left to the Government. There are exceptions; a few large plantation companies concerned with tropical crops put a lot of money into plant breeding, often with outstanding success, as when the Sudanese cotton crop was saved by the breeding of a variety resistant to a bacterial disease called "black arm". While the chemical firms have spent many millions on research, for every £100 of agricultural products sold in the United Kingdom, the Government spends one penny on research of all kinds, animal and vegetable. The total devoted to all forms of scientific study of our food supplies is about £3½ million, compared with over £45 million for non-military nuclear research.

Many insects have predators—those little fleas on the backs of big fleas of the nursery jingle; wood-wasps that lay their eggs in grubs, ladybirds that eat aphids, and so on. Wide-spectrum sprays, as they are called—the general-purpose ones like DDT—obliterate all insects, whether harmful or not. But selective sprays will destroy the grub of one particular species of (say) moth, and not the wasp that preys on it; kill the aphis and not the ladybird; and so on. Those the spray does not eradicate, the predator will; nature and chemical co-operate. Some such selective chemicals have already been synthesised. These are the systemic compounds, which get right inside the plant, suffuse it, and so make it poisonous to a particular kind of insect, for instance to the aphis family who suck the sap.

That is one line of attack. There are others. One, a pretty low trick on the face of it, is to synthesise what are called sex attractants. A number of female insects attract their mates by smell; sometimes the males can pick up the scent even through plate glass. An example is the gypsy moth, a pest of forest trees. In North America, spraying with DDT did more harm to birds, bees and other creatures than to the gypsy moths. Then a group of researchers synthesised a chemical so like the female moth's attractant that it fooled the males. On a small scale, you can smear this chemical on sticky surfaces and then trap and kill the males, leaving a mass of sex-starved females who cannot breed. On the larger scale you can spray the attractant on the forests from the air, hoping that it will so confuse the males they will lose their heads, like stag-hounds distracted with aniseed by the League Against Cruel Sports, and fail to find their mates. This has worked fairly well in the United States. Food-imitating smells have also been tried, but insects do not find these nearly so attractive as the odours connected with sex.

Researchers turn the insects' sexual urges against them in other ways. They sterilise males and then release them; the insects mate, but nothing comes of it; this has been tried with some success on tsetse flies in Africa. A kind of blowfly called the screw-worm was eradicated first in Curacao, and then in Florida, where about $3\frac{1}{2}$ thousand *million* screw-worms were bred, sterilised by means of gamma-rays, and released from aircraft. The screw-worm has disappeared, at any rate for the time being. These were combined operations by biologists and chemists in the case of attractants, and biologists and physicists in the screw-worm example. This seems the most hopeful line—"integrated control", a combination of methods, but one that always brings in the biologist who deals with living creatures, and whose aim is to maintain a balance between them, not simply to dispense death on all sides.

His particular contribution may be the method known as biological control: the use of predators to keep down the pest's numbers. There have been many successful examples of this. One of the earliest goes back to 1888, when Australian *Vedalia* beetles, transported to California, within two years controlled a scale insect that had been causing havoc among citrus fruit. The pest had come from Australia in the first place, so the beetles were merely catching up. In recent years, DDT was used on these same Californian citrus orchards to combat other insect pests. The scale insects did not mind the DDT, but the *Vedalia* beetles succumbed, and things were back to square one. Now more *Vedalia* beetles have been brought over from Australia.

Chinese citrus growers of antiquity established in their orchards colonies of ants to prey on harmful caterpillars, and provided them with bamboo runways to enable them to get from tree to tree. Arabs in the Yemen brought predacious ants down from the mountains to pray on lesser ants who preyed on date-palms. These are valid examples of biological control. More recently, insect predators have been moved about the world to tackle pests of eucalyptus trees in South Africa, apples in New Zealand, sugar cane in Hawaii, coconuts in Fiji, and Russian cabbages.

Hitherto, biological control has not done much to help us in Britain with our pests, which are considerably less troublesome than in countries where crops are grown on a much larger scale. We have, however, seen one outstanding example: myxomatosis in rabbits, caused by a virus bred to attack them. It controlled the rabbits but horrified us, and so we quickly outlawed it.

Fouling Our Nest

WILD life in Britain is threatened from two directions. On the one hand, we are fouling our nest with our social and industrial excreta—residues of pesticides, effluent of factories, radio-active fallout, oil discharge from tankers, exhaust fumes from road vehicles, discarded cars (6,000 of them dumped last year), and all the other unattractive by-products of humanity's industrial activities. If all the solid effluent in the world, someone has calculated, were piled into a heap, a single year's output would make a mountain 20,000 feet high with vertical sides, sixteen square miles in extent on top. Ours has become, indeed, an effluent society.

In the second place we are changing, distorting and destroying the habitat of our surviving birds and beasts, not only by taking land for building and roads, flooding it with reservoirs and covering it with pylons, though plenty of that too, but by the mere dispersal of ourselves. Each man kills the thing he loves, and mobs of humans murder solitude.

To glance first at the nest-fouling. By every post the Nature Conservancy's laboratories near Huntingdon receive dead birds, whose fat is extracted from the breast muscles or livers and analysed. Residues of the organo-chlorines are frequently found. Amongst aquatic birds, herons have the most, grebes next and moorhens very little; amongst land birds, sparrow-hawks the most, owls rather less, wood-pigeons almost nil. Always it is the predators that have the highest poisonous residues. The reason is the food-chain. Fish caught seventy miles out to sea contain dieldrin which must have been washed down from the residues of sprays into the rivers, and passed through a whole series of plants and animals, the concentration mounting at each stage. The eggs and corpses of shags, guillemots, kittiwakes, puffins, gulls and oyster-catchers found dead or addled off St Abb's Head had up to 8·9 parts per million of organo-chlorine residues in their fat or yolk which they, in turn, can have derived only from their diet of fish.

The higher the position of the animal in the food-chain, the more poison it gets. Ground beetles resident in soil that had been sprayed with dieldrin and DDT lay on their backs twitching for up to forty-eight hours, thus tempting skylarks, who gobbled up too many and died. (Death of a lark: "although it lacked muscular co-ordination and could not fly or stand, it continued to beat its wings and clutch with its toes while lying on its side".) It is always the predator at the top of the food-chain who is the most vulnerable. A little of what you fancy does you good, but a lot of nothing else does you in.

Most British birds of prey are declining in numbers, especially peregrine falcons, kites, sparrow-hawks and golden eagles, because they are failing to breed. Every single predator's egg so far examined in the Conservancy's laboratories has contained pesticide residues; and so, in 1963-64, did every one of eighty-two analysed marine birds' eggs. Up to 1939, about 650 pairs of peregrines bred regularly in Britain. During the war they were severely hammered in order to protect carrier pigeons, but when it was over they were themselves protected, and their numbers built up again. In 1955 a new decline set in, and in 1962 only sixty-eight pairs hatched their young. By now only a very few isolated pairs of peregrines remain in England and Wales, and most of these fail to breed successfully. Some survive in Scotland, but here, too, they are laying smaller clutches and hatching fewer chicks.

The same story is being told in all parts of the planet. At an international conference of wild-lifers held in 1964 at Caen, evidence came forward from all over Europe of the serious decline of the eagle-owl, peregrine, marsh harrier, goshawk, golden eagle, short-toed eagle and kite—again, the hard-hit predators.

All this has coincided with the spread of pesticides. Organo-chlorine residues have been found in the eggs. This is not cast-iron proof, but as circumstantial evidence it could hardly be stronger. Experiments on game birds in America have shown that small but prolonged doses of organo-chlorine compounds decrease the hatchability of their eggs, and that more of the chicks which do hatch out survive only for a few hours or days. "The contamination of the peregrine population," affirms Dr D. A. Ratcliffe, the organiser of a survey conducted by the British Trust for Ornithology, "is now demonstrated beyond doubt by the finding of residues of dieldrin, heptachlor, BHC and DDT in every one of twelve eggs from eleven different eyries. A peregrine found dead on Lundy Island contained seventy-eight p.p.m. of total chlorinated hydrocarbon in its liver"—a more-than-lethal dose. Sparrow-hawks and buzzards are also sitting on infertile eggs. Sheep dips and sprays are gnerally blamed.

While infertility in eggs caused by chemical pesticides is a major reason for the decline of predators, it is not the only one. Drainage and tidying up of "wetlands" has hit such birds as marsh harriers; cities and conurbations spreading over the countryside destroy the wild places where such birds nest and hunt; it is said that farmers nowadays shoot more birds of prey. And the prey itself is tending to disappear; in France alone, two million gun licences are issued every year. Every man's hand is against the predator, supposedly the foe of sheep and game birds. But is he really such an enemy? A study made by Dr David Jenkins of predation on a Scottish grouse moor at first blackened the golden eagles, harriers and foxes who, between them, killed five hundred grouse in five years. But closer studies showed that seven out of every eight of the grouse they had destroyed were birds without territories, who were in any case doomed to die without issue. What is loosely known as "the balance of nature" appears, on investigation, to be a lot more intricate and subtle than we at first supposed. The predator does not destroy his habitat, or eat himself out of house and home, but himself helps to maintain and strengthen the species he preys upon by weeding out the weaker, diseased or injured individuals, so encouraging only the fittest to survive.

Once Britain was almost wholly covered by forest and that is when our bird population evolved. Of our fifty major land species, about forty are still basically woodland birds. Now woods cover less than five per cent of our land, the lowest proportion in Europe and one of the lowest in the world. The birds have taken to the hedgerows. They are all right there, but if the hedgerows go, they will not be; they are unlikely to adapt themselves to barley prairies, or to nest in electric fences, feedlots and barbed wire. Chaffinches, blackbirds, thrushes, wrens, robins, tits, goldfinches, all would go. We might keep some partridges, lapwings, skylarks and corn buntings, and most waterfowl; otherwise we would be reduced to pigeons, starlings and sparrows, with crows and jackdaws thrown in.

Are the hedgerows seriously threatened? Yes, they are. We have an estimated 616,000 miles of hedge covering about half a million acres, and containing a lot of trees. Most hedges were planted between 100 and 150 years ago, but about one-third are older, and there is one at Charlton, in Wiltshire, mentioned in a deed of A.D. 861.

The economic usefulness of hedges is mainly over. The high cost of labour, massive farm machinery, electric fences, the need to exploit every acre, all these combine to make most hedges not merely useless, but a liability. So they are being bulldozed out intentionally, accidentally damaged as a by-product of the spreading practice of burning straw instead of conserving it, and cut mechanically, which kills young trees.

Between one-tenth and one-fifth of our hedges have gone over the last twenty years. The fathers of the present generation of farmers often paid their men a shilling for every hedgerow sapling they spared. Now hedging has been mechanised and pretty soon there will be no more hedgerow trees. The Nature Conservancy made a sample survey in the east Midlands and found that for every ten miles of hedge existing in 1947, only four miles remained in 1964. "If it was not for the shooting," the sampler said, "in that area there would be no hedges left at all. Sporting farmers keep them to shelter game birds and offer nesting places. And the Belvoir hunt have preserved *all* their fences." The paradox that it is the men who want to kill animals who keep them alive is, anyway in this instance, quite true.

If a hedge is not burnt or bulldozed, then it is mechanically clipped and sprayed. Naturalists believe that butterfly populations have fallen mainly because so many of the hedgerow wildflowers have disappeared. The loss of charlock, cornflowers, poppies, wild geranium, meadowsweet and many docks, thistles and nettles may not worry farmers, but those insects who lived on and bred in them diminish, and so affect the birds who ate *them*—another food-chain. "Nobody has attempted to measure the ecological effect of herbicides," Dr Norman Moore of the Nature Conservancy has written. "Those hedges and ponds, roadside verges and railway embankments which survive are a national asset and should be preserved." But they are not. Over one thousand farm ponds have been filled in.

The same with the rushy verges of canals and streams. Once we had over forty species of dragonfly, now about half of these are very rare and may become extinct. Dredging of brooks and fens, piping of roadside ditches, installing of sewage plants, have obliterated many of their breeding sites. Since 1940, nearly one-third of our botanically rich old pasture has gone, to be replaced by cereals or by leys containing less than half a dozen grasses— agricultural progress, but ecological impoverishment.

If Hardy's native were to return today to "the vast tract of unenclosed wild known as Egdon Heath", instead of an ochred reddleman trudging beside a van drawn by two shaggy ponies across a "sombre stretch of rounds and hollows that seemed to rise and meet the evening gloom in pure sympathy", he would find himself dodging buses between housing estates, bumping into War Department installations or hemmed in by the Forestry Commission's dripping conifers. The actual heathland, the wild and solitary part, has shrunk from about 75,000 acres in 1811 to some 25,000 acres today, and been split into over a hundred bits and pieces. Most of this has come about in the last fifty years; the heath altered little between the start and finish of the nineteenth century. If the native were to put off his return a few years longer he would find virtually no heath at all; big forestry and building schemes are planned for most of the surviving patches. Two tiny areas have been set aside as nature reserves.

A number of the wild plants and animals are on the way out, and a few have gone already—five varieties of vascular plant, black game, and the natterjack toad. On the other hand fallow-roe and sika deer have been added, and of course a great many conifers. A century ago, the Dartford warbler was to be found from Norfolk down to Cornwall; today an estimated 425 pairs survive in Dorset and Hampshire, and that is all. The sand lizard and the smooth snake are getting very scarce and the Dorset heath has been driven into corners by the Forestry Commission and needs protection if it is to survive.

Most herbicides sprayed on hedges and roadside verges do not persist as the organo-chlorides do, and so do not directly harm birds and insects, but they do make drastic changes in the habitat. Along the Roman Akeman Street in Gloucestershire, a wide-verged and now minor road, twelve years' annual spraying of the verges has knocked out nettles, thistles, docks and broad-leaved weeds like hedge parsley, cow parsnip and hogweed, together with the coarse, tufty grasses such as cocksfoot and tall oat-grass. In their place have come small plants with finer leaves like the fescues and meadow-grasses (*Poa* spp.) that do not grow nearly so tall.

Some wild flowers have vanished, but not all; ladies' bedstraw, toadflax, blue scabious, white milk vetch, campion and speedwell survive, and primroses, aconites and violets are not affected, because they flower before it is time to spray, and show up better once the coarse, stemmy plants have gone. There is no doubt that spraying tidies up the verges, giving them a lawn-like look well suited to the folding tables and chairs, the plates and cups of modern roadside picnics, much more elegant than an undisciplined tangle of nettles, burdock and brushwood, thistles and briars. Not much comfort there for insects, however, or birds and bumble-bees, and in unsprayed verges and hedgerows there is a very much greater variety of plants. Chemicals narrow the range, reduce the biological potential of the habitat—more and more of less and less.

A strip of ground totally bare of all vegetation runs along one of the verges of Akeman Street: not a blade, not a shoot. This has been treated by a total eradicator (not a hormone) for use on paths. "It even changes the soil structure, turns it into a fine dust where seeds will not germinate." For how long? "At least a season; the effect wears off gradually, but tends to be cumulative over the years." Next time anyone has a scorched earth policy in mind, aerial spraying with this chemical would serve the purpose well.

If roadside verges do not get kept in order by synthetic growth-regulating hormones, they are liable to be saturated with lead from the exhausts of cars and lorries, or tickled up with radio-active dust. The anti-knock component used in petrol (lead tetraethyl) annually discharges along our highways some 2,850 tons of lead, which can be highly poisonous, and the combustion of coal adds another 30,000 tons to the general atmosphere. On top of that there is a lot of molybdenum about, which can be even more poisonous than lead. Both these indestructible elements, taken up through the roots of plants, get into leaves and stems, pass on through the cycle, and must be building up in the soil very slowly, but at a rate that will accelerate as the process goes on.

Then there is the fall-out from nuclear weapon tests. Strontium-90 and Caesium-137 are the two of most significance. After a bout of testing, there is a time-lag while the fission material drifts about and is distributed by rainfall over our pastures and crops; roughly one-quarter of all that is washed down from heaven gets into the plants. The wetter regions receive most, partly because of their heavier rainfall but also because the particles find their way more readily into the coarse grasses and bogs, rushes and bracken and tussocks of the hills than into cereals and more open swards.

In 1962, the amount of Strontium-90 in the rainfall shot up by three times, and the quantity in our milk just about doubled. We got more in cabbages, cheese and tea, but less in eggs and flour, probably because most of the corn belonged to the previous harvest. Nevertheless, the level reached in our food was still well below the safety limit fixed by our watchdog in these matters, the Medical Research Council. In milk, the degree of contamination is expressed as the ratio of Strontium-90 to calcium in picocuries per gram. The M.R.C. allows us 130 of these units on average for the whole population, including infants, but considers 400 pc safe for any given individual. In 1962, the average was only 12 pc, less than eight per cent of the permissible quantity. In 1963, contamination of our milk by Strontium-90 reached over 25 pc, compared with under 12 pc the year before, but still only one-fifth of the danger level.

This Plimsoll line of danger must, inevitably, be a guess, since doctors carry out their tests on animals, not humans; we can be sure their guess allows a wide margin of safety. Reindeer in Canada living largely on lichens, organisms with an especially high capacity for absorbing radio-active material, have been found to have in their bones up to twelve times the upper limit of the dose considered safe for humans, without coming to any apparent harm. In 1964, United States authorities found that Eskimos in northern Alaska had an average level of 1,170 micropicocuries of Caesium-137 in their bodies, rising to as much as 2,200 in one individual, thus exceeding the average safety "guideline" of 1,000 mcp established by the Federal Radiation Council, though not the maximum level of 3,000 mpc for any one individual. This fall-out level was about 100 times higher than in the rest of the United States and resulted from another food-chain: lichens absorbed the Caesium-137, caribou ate the lichens and the Eskimos ate the caribou.

These fission products retain their radio-activity in the soil for a long time. Just how long must depend on circumstances, so we cannot be sure, but the half-life of Strontium-90 has been put at twenty-six years. Whether it is radio-active particles, toxic chemicals, synthetic hormones, lead, molybdenum—in the end everything must come to rest in the soil or sea. To what extent will all these residues accumulate, as dieldrin has been shown to do? And what about the soil animals, down there in their billions—insects, worms, spiders, mites, nematodes, every kind of creature? How will they like being drenched in chemicals?

Now that most of the organo-chlorines are to be withdrawn, more of the organo-phosphates, which are not nearly so persistent, will be used instead. But earthworms, which do not seem to mind the former, quickly succumb to some of the latter, such as parathion. While less persistent than the dieldrin group these are just as deadly, if not more so, to the nervous system. Some years ago a flock of sheep strayed into a field of sugar beet that had been recently sprayed with an organo-phosphate, and forty-nine out of sixty died. In Indiana, parathion spraying killed an estimated 65,000 red-winged blackbirds and starlings. Even some of the hormone weed-killers, supposedly so harmless to everything but weeds, have begun to look a little less benign. "I could take you to a field," said a veterinary surgeon, "that was littered with dead earthworms the day after it was sprayed. In my opinion, some of the synthetic hormones persist in the soil for up to five years." Hitherto this opinion has not been put to the test by scientific experiment. In the opinion of Dr B. N. K. Davis of the Nature Conservancy, "our soils are becoming reservoirs of persistent and potentially dangerous chemicals, and the means by which these find their way into birds and fish are still largely matters of conjecture".

Finally, bees. In fruit-growing regions, it is the practice for bee-keepers to move their hives from orchard to orchard to coincide with the blossom. When organo-phosphates first came into use, the bees took a terrible beating and the fruit-growers took alarm. Some orchards, it was said, were almost carpeted with dead and dying insects. Now the pest-control contractors warn the apiarists when and where they are going to spray, and honey-bees are shut into their hives until the danger is over. Wild bees, however, cannot be shut up, and suffer grievous loss.

Bumble-bees pollinate several commercial crops like red clover, lucerne and field beans. (A formidable task: at the peak period, one acre of red clover will develop up to forty-five million florets in one day.) Having longer tongues than honey-bees, they can reach right down into the base of the flower for the nectar, and honey-bees can-not. Sometimes they cheat, and bite a hole in the base of the floret's tube. It is nearly always the shorter-tongued varieties of bumble-bee, maddened no doubt by frustra-tion, who take to biting these holes. Observers doubt if this is an instinct, but think the bees work it out for themselves and even remember the trick from year to year. Not so dumb, bumble-bees. But hard to count, and firm proof is lacking that their numbers have declined. Most people think they have, and that it is affecting the yield of field beans. So a search has been started for a way to by-pass the bumble-bee by breeding a do-it-yourself bean. In 1956, plant breeders at Aberystwyth got hold of a single, self-pollinating tick-bean plant, and crossed it with varieties from Persia and the Mediterranean regions. Now they have self-fertile lines of promise, and, if all goes well, we clever mortals will succeed in eliminating both the bumble-bees, and the need for their co-operation in our husbandry.

14

Grooves of Change

Anyone who has read as far as this will have got a false impression: Britain as a land of factory farms run by ruthless agribusinessmen and money-mad tycoons, all vertically integrated; a countryside dotted with avian prisons, feed-lots full of liver-abscessed calves surrounded by hedgeless barley-prairies, drenched with poisonous chemicals and littered with dead birds. The shortest of Sunday spins in the family car will convince him that he has been misled. We have been looking at trends, and anyone who attempts this must present a false picture because he must pick out what are still the exceptions, the growing-points. He is guessing at the pattern as it may appear in ten, twenty, an unpredictable number of years time, not as it is now.

He may, of course, be wrong about the trends, which can be arrested, reversed, slowed down or speeded up. This may happen: but only, one would suppose, as part of a much larger change in the direction of our civilisation as a whole. It seems unlikely to overtake only that sector of society dealing with our food supplies. On the contrary, for some time this sector has been lagging behind the rest of the nation, and a catching up is overdue. So it looks as if agribusiness will snowball, integration spread its tentacles, technology accelerate. Farming in this country, Mr Tristram Beresford has pointed out, is ripening for revolution. Up to date it "has not had an industrial revolution; it has been mechanised, but that is another thing. Essentially it is still a craft, still in the 'domestic' stage. And the forces now threatening to substitute competition for regulation and protection are

145

like waters building up behind a dam. Before long the dam will give. Then the waters will break through and usher in agriculture's brave new world."[1]

Meanwhile we are still a country of small family farms managed on traditional lines. In England and Wales there are about 345,000 agricultural holdings, of which just about three-quarters are less than 100 acres and nearly six out of ten under 50 acres. About one-third are family farms, employing no regular labour, whose owners or tenants derive their whole livelihood from the farm. Of the remainder, 58,000 are larger commercial farms employing anywhere from one to fifty men. Only 2,000 are farm businesses run by companies or tycoons of the kind we have been discussing.

Men are leaving the land at the rate of some 20,000 a year, and mechanisation is rapidly increasing. Lumping farmers and their men together, just under one million, less than four per cent of the working population, remain on the land. Like the predators, their numbers are shrinking; so, indeed, is the land they cultivate, at present by about 50,000 acres annually, but the rate, like that of growth of population, is rising year by year. Here and there are pockets of resistance: a recent survey of 7,000 small farms in Wales showed that sixty per cent of the farmers had a son or sons working on the land who wanted to take over from their fathers.

Small as our farms may be, they are, on average, considerably larger than those of our fellow-Europeans. In the six members of the European Economic Community, there are seven million holdings of which three out of four are smaller than 25 acres. Most of us think of Germany as a land of large, efficient, centralised units, whatever may be the occupation in which its people engage; while this may be true of industry, German

[1] *Financial Times* Annual Review, July 6, 1964.

farms are even smaller than ours, averaging only 18½ acres. Well over half their farms are under 12 acres, and the owners mostly work at other jobs as well. Nearly forty per cent are classed as family farms of between 12 and 50 acres, leaving under nine per cent for larger holdings of 50 acres and upwards.[1] As in all Western countries, the trend is towards the larger unit; in the last twelve years the number of holdings has declined by 360,000 to a present total of about 1·6 million. The number of family farms of between 12 and 50 acres has actually increased, if only slightly. At the same time, more and more people have been migrating to the cities. As recently as 1950, some 7 million Germans lived and worked on the land; by 1960 this was down to 5·8 millions, a loss of 1·2 million people. And during this period Western Germany had managed to absorb nearly ten million homeless, destitute and often starving refugees from Eastern Europe. Since then a steady stream, amounting to over 2½ million, has arrived from the Soviet zone.

So agribusiness has a long way to go in Western Europe, and there is a good deal of feeling against it. Holland passed a law in 1933 limiting to three hundred the number of hens that might be kept on any single holding, with the aim of protecting the small man. In 1962, however, this had to be repealed, because Dutch poultrymen could no longer compete with mass production in Germany.

The Federal German Government, and the governments of the various *Länder*, have as their policy the development of the middle-sized family farm, and do not want the factory-farm to get a grip. There are proposals to limit the number of animals that may be

[1] The actual figures are: Under 5 hectares (12 acres) 51·7%; from 5–20 h (12–50 acres), 39·4%; over 20 h (50 acres), 8·9%.

kept on any given holding; not, once more, in the interests of the animals, but in order to preserve family farms. So far these are proposals only, and the difficulties of applying them may well prove too great to be overcome.

In other ways the Germans appear to be heading in a direction contrary to our own. Whereas we go on bulldozing hedges and cutting down trees, the Germans are planting new ones, at any rate in certain areas; in Schleswig-Holstein nearly 9,000 miles of hedge and shelter-belt have been added in the last few years. German policy is to consolidate as many as possible of their mini-holdings into units of around forty acres, and on these their planning laws provide for hedges, coppices and pockets of shrubs. They want a diversified landscape, not barley prairies; one that is pleasing to the eye as well as to the purse.

The underlying aim of this is social, not economic. The image of the independent, sturdy, hard-working family farmer is admired. It is felt he adds a sorely needed ballast to urban societies everywhere becoming more unpredictable, hedonistic and even hysterical: his son sits usefully upon a tractor instead of screaming at the Beatles, and he himself retains a set of values which, as we increasingly abandon them, appear more and more desirable.

One thing he retains is the power to make decisions. What with weather, fluctuating markets, the wilfulness of animals, the vagaries of crops, in one way or another he is making decisions every moment of the day. He is a master, if only of an acre or two, a few fowls, a cow, and himself; not a slave. This imparts character. Farmers do not always have nice characters by any means, but that does not matter; it is character we want to hang on to in a world in which ours has been constantly eroded, and now seems about to be crushed into almost total uniformity by machines.

Bit by bit, ever since the start of the industrial revolution, we have been retreating from our concept of quality and excellence, and advancing towards a set of values based on quantity; now we approach the quantitive society, whose dominant values are material. The small farmer is felt, not always correctly, to occupy a pocket of resistance to all this. His set of values is not wholly materialistic; he will work long hours for poor rewards because he is doing something useful, something fundamental, something he enjoys; for him there is more to life than Friday's pay-packet and instalments on a new car. So let us not see the last small, independent farmer squeezed out by city bankers, tycoons, combines and trusts buying up land to salt away their money, dodge death duties, establish cartels and monopolies and sacrifice everything to the golden calf.

It is, of course, quite possible to preserve anything, from ancient monuments and historic houses to stretches of coastline and small farmers, if we really want to, and are prepared to pay. It always costs money. We pay something already to preserve the small farmer through the agricultural subsidies. There could hardly be a clumsier way of doing it. No system based on price support can be devised which does not benefit the big producer more than the small, because he has got more to sell and produces it more cheaply; Mr Eastwood expects to draw £5 million in egg subsidy, and at present we pay for one-third of the agribusinessman's slap-up environmentally-controlled buildings, in order to help the small man patch up his barn. Two-thirds of the subsidies go to one-third of the (larger) farmers, and the single-handed milk producer gets no subsidy at all.

It would be very much simpler, cheaper and more

effective merely to divide out amongst the small farmers the sum we are prepared to pay for their preservation. People who can ill afford it keep Alsatians, and there are millions of budgerigars. The small farmer is a sort of national pet; as there are comparatively few, the cost of keeping them would not be prohibitive, and they would be much less trouble than Alsatians; they produce meat as well as consuming it, and do not need to be taken out for walks.

Not only that, many of them (though not all) like to keep their land in good heart. This is a fuzzy concept, a quality judgement which would puzzle a computer; it may not be economic, but does create a bank of fertility. Intensive methods drive the soil's capacity to the top of its bent—that is their object; therefore, they cannot leave any significant reserve. It is always dangerous to operate anything without reserves. So there is a case to be made out for keeping on small farmers not merely as pets but as caretakers, continuing to produce things on non-intensive, or on semi-intensive, lines; fattening and milking their cattle on grass, rotating their crops, running sheep on the hills and even keeping free-range hens. Few small farmers are likely to make a decent living, by modern standards, in this fashion, let alone enjoy a modicum of leisure; they would have to be subsidised; but, as pets-cum-guardians, they might earn their keep.

There is another argument, only to be mentioned in a whisper because it is at the best frivolous, at the worst rather rude. It is concerned with beauty, in itself a dubious word: the beauty of our countryside. If we preserve small farmers we shall also preserve their farms. These add to, indeed constitute, a landscape pleasing to the eye; this in turn attracts swelling hordes of tourists, who come not to see our office blocks and bungalows and motorways, which are just the same as their own, but our picturesque ceremonies and the beauties of our country-side. So family farmers have almost as much value to the tourist industry as the changing of the Guard: beauty can be priced, and honour saved.

Even if we preserve some small farmers, we shall not reverse the general trend, which is determined not by our wishes but by our fecundity. Hunger goads technology, technology twists the soil's tail. More and more of less and less. Need it all be so gloomy? Cannot progress be enjoyed for a change? Fixing a robust, satiric eye upon the crystal ball, Mr Tristram Beresford has glimpsed a brave new world in which the milking cow has vanished and our milk is synthesised in automated factories from grass, weeds and crop residues, and all the food we need is grown on about one-third of the land we are using now, transformed into hedgeless, treeless corn prairies, with its crop yields doubled or trebled by plant breeders, fertilisers and sprays. Our animal proteins—broilers, barley-fed calves, fat lambs—will be forced in huge feed-lots with strict environmental control, and the calves bred, as in Texas or Australia, in ranching herds. All this will leave about two-thirds of our land free from the demands of intensive production. Here is our playground, an enormous national park.

There must, of course, be cities, but these will be planned, sited and controlled, and obliged to grow upwards and not outwards into a subtopian sprawl. In their copious leisure (three day, two day working week?) people will repair to the national parks. There will be great reservoirs to sail and fish on, attracting droves of birds; forests full of game, and much more wildlife all round; native deer to be hunted (the venison would make a change from barley-beef) and exotic species introduced. The Poles have successfully re-introduced bison; we could do the same.

Man the hunter will re-appear; there will be camping sites, gliding clubs, Outward Bound centres, mountaineers, a staff of green-clad rangers. Amid all this, if somewhat sandwiched between industrial cities, conurbations and motorways, will range our breeding herds which, like humans, thrive better out of doors. They, and we, will at last be free of stress, or freer than we are now. Private farms will disappear, and private rights in land.

One man's fantasy; there are others, perhaps more likely and certainly less comely, involving urban sprawl, vistas of bungalows, subtopias, up-ended matchbox office blocks, pylons, refineries, sewage plants and cemeteries of old cars. Either way, we are in for changes; either way, a lot of animals must stay indoors.

It's no good asking the Computer

WE all know that men are lords of creation. *And let them have dominion over the fish of the sea, and over the fowl of the air, and over the cattle, and over all the earth, and over every creeping thing that creepeth upon the earth.* Men have got dominion all right. We also know dominion carries responsibilities. How men are to use power without corruption and without abuse of each other has been, and is, what history has always been about, what a large part of morals and ethics are about, an unsolved dilemma. We are concerned here with man's dominion over other kinds of living creature—but still creatures and still living, who share with him the resources of the planet, its earth and air and water, its potential miseries and joys. *And to every beast of the earth, and to every fowl of the air, and to every thing that creepeth upon the earth, wherein there is life, I have given every green herb for meat.*

The whole question of our treatment of our fellow species is like a path through a bog, ringed about with sentiment and false analogy and sublimated guilt. We domesticated animals in order to eat them and their products, not to keep them as pets. They are there to be eaten. No one questions that. (At least, only a few vegetarians.) Nor can the fact be questioned that they must to some extent be confined—one cannot have them roaming round the streets like Indian cattle. Then they must be killed. Our concern merely is to see that this is done without inflicting on the beasts more pain and discomfort than is necessary.

Hitherto, our main obligations on this score have been to make the actual process of slaughter as painless as possible, and to prevent individual men inflicting pain on individual animals. For this purpose we have passed laws which have been at least partially obeyed, and in the main supported by public opinion. But of course cruelty has gone on. The emergence of factory farming has inclined people to the assumption that there is something new in keeping animals shut up in cramped conditions, very often in the dark. There is nothing new in it at all.

Anyone who has been about on farms has seen calves tethered by the neck in the dark, stinking corners of old, ill-ventilated sheds, often dirty and bothered by flies. Pigs have been tucked into tiny, filthy styes, as cramped as sweat-boxes, hens have moped in dilapidated, un-cleaned coops, sheep suffered torments from blowfly and footrot. You have only to see a terrified and therefore obstinate cow being beaten and tail-twisted and generally dragooned into a lorry to recognise ill-treatment in the old-fashioned, traditional manner. I recall my own feel-ings when a young bull reared from birth to enjoy, per-haps, more freedom than a bull should enjoy (he was of a placid breed), was sold to a neighbouring farmer, kept tightly tethered in a stall night and day and never released except to perform his function, all over in ten minutes. The bull may not have minded, but I did.

And there is one of the treacherous places in the bog. Just as we have made God in our own image, we put our own minds into animals; as we think and feel, so do they. How true is this? "Human language is especially con-structed to describe the mental states of human beings," a psychologist, Dr Stout, has written, "and this means that it is especially constructed so as to mislead us when we attempt to describe the working of minds that differ in a great degree from our own."

On the other hand, in so far as animals may be pre-sumed to live less by reason and more by instinct than we do, the frustration of what we may assume to be natural instincts—freedom of movement and free choice of food, ability to stretch wings and dust feathers, to suckle young, to mate, to live with others of the species in a well-defined social order—such frustration might cause more, not less, discomfiture. We do not know, and no animal can tell us, except by going to the extreme of falling sick. And to this we attribute wholly physical causes.

Here, again, we may be wrong. Until very recently, veterinary medicine has been stuck at the stage occupied by human medicine when lunatics were chained in Bedlam and strapped into strait-jackets. The influence of mind on body has been almost completely ignored. The science of animal behaviour and psychology perhaps will do for animal medicine what pioneers in human psychology and the treatment of mental disorders did for our own species. Another of those break-throughs may be imminent. Then we may know a great deal more than we do now about how animals think, feel and react to treatment. We could scarcely know less.

What has happened is that factory farming has transferred the whole matter to another plane. If an individual farmer neglected a calf tied up in a corner, or a sow in her backyard lean-to, that was a matter between him and a single animal; and if an R.S.P.C.A. inspector could catch him at it, he would find himself in court. If something goes wrong with the ventilation in a beef-lot or battery and 1,000 calves suffocate, or 10,000 hens, it is the scale that makes the event more horrifying; the degree of human cruelty or neglect may in itself be less.

Most prosecutions for cruelty to animals are brought by the R.S.P.C.A. But the Society's inspectors have no power of entry on to private premises, including farms, and this has always hampered them. Farmers seldom like inspectors of anything poking about; still less often do they deliberately invite one to gather evidence of a misdemeanour, in order to prosecute.

Factory farms are surely betrayed by their description. If they really are factories, like others they should be open to inspection. A manufacturer cannot refuse the right of entry to a Home Office inspector; nor should a factory farmer, just because he turns out eggs or meat instead of nails or refrigerators, be able to keep out a properly accredited official. Reform would involve a change in the status of R.S.P.C.A. inspectors, perhaps their being taken over by a Ministry.

Inspectors are the last stage, not the first. They enforce the law, they do not make it; and the present laws are out of date, too vague and limited to apply to the new world of factory farms. What is needed is a set of standards. So much space per bird perhaps, x cubic feet per calf, y degree of illumination. It is all very arbitrary, and most of the knowledge on which any decisions of this kind should be based simply is not there, and would be out of date in ten years if it was. Legislators will have to guess, and will not always guess correctly. They will have to compromise. This applies to most human attempts to be fair, humane and dignified, yet not sentimental, unrealistic or too much like King Canute.

All such regulations, however carefully designed, must beg the central question: is this the right way to keep animals at all? What about that "tenderness toward all living creatures made subject to us" to which John Woolmer referred a couple of centuries ago? Are the imperatives of our rising population, our diminishing resources and our hungry stomachs in conflict with our ethics, our responsibilities, and with something even deeper connected with our spiritual satisfactions and needs? If that is so, can this conflict be resolved?

If we continue to multiply and try to improve our material standards of living, then we must sacrifice not merely the freedom, and perhaps the decency, of domestic animals, but also a part, at least, of our own spiritual need for a relationship of mutual respect and enrichment between ourselves and the plants and animals and natural features of our planet. With these, we have hitherto existed in a kind of symbiosis by which each fructified the other. "There is night and day, brother, both sweet things; sun, moon and stars, brother, all sweet things; there is likewise a wind on the heath." But not in the environmentally-controlled battery house and feedlot, sweat-box and broiler house.

Belonging, as we do, to a species ineffably egocentric, the aspect of the matter that most distresses those who feel any distress is not so much whether we are being cruel to animals, as whether being cruel to animals is bad for us. It is like the argument advanced against hanging people, that it is harmful to the prison officers. Dignitories of the Church declaim against factory farming on the grounds that being beastly to the beasts is degrading to humans. Treating animals as machines takes us farther from a natural order ordained, in the belief of churchmen, by God, or, in the view of biologists, deriving from an ecological balance achieved through evolution; in either case, it takes us closer to machines created by man: machines which tend more and more to possess and control their creator, as Mary Shelley foretold they would, whiling away a wet summer by writing *Frankenstein* in Switzerland in 1816.

Any living creature is interesting so long as it is an individual, or else one of a community, like bees, observing a wonderfully intricate and well-directed set of rules. As one of an orderless mob, the pattern and the purpose goes, chaos is come again, respect forfeited. Perhaps it is all bound up with what Dr Albert Schweitzer calls reverence, or respect, for life. What finishes respect is when a creature, man or beast, ceases to be an individual and becomes one of a mass. The mob destroys reason, dignity and order, and substitutes hysteria, cruelty and panic; it is the abrogation of the mind. Single lemmings are no doubt interesting, lively and affectionate creatures; migrating lemmings, obscene. The Balinese keep single grasshoppers in little bamboo cages, feed and tend them, bet on their prowess when they spar with other grass-hoppers and no doubt enjoy the music they make with their rough legs. A swarm of locusts is another thing.

Is that what is wrong, sheer numbers? Plagues of caterpillars, clouds of birds, proliferating cancer cells, floods of men? Driving us on towards the things we fear and hate—stress, vast urban agglomerations, automa-tion, mass-production, noise, submergence, uniformity, and treating living creatures as machines? Pressures threaten to flatten out our personalities, our individual powers to make decisions, to triumph and to suffer, to chose, to create, to contemplate or command.

Trapped ourselves, we in turn trap the animals, con-fining them in our own faceless world in which our highest adventure is to reach a moon with no life on it, covered in dust. Deceived by a false respect not for life, for a chain of being in which death has a constructive part, but for ourselves, for our mere existence, our bodily survival—to this we sacrifice our souls. Willy-nilly, the animals are in the same boat. We put them there, and do not know how to get them out.

Something has got left out, a missing factor; a broken link, a snapped silver cord. *"Though I understand all mysteries, and all knowledge, and though I have all faith, so that I could move mountains, and have not charity. . . ."* Could that be what is missing? That old-fashioned grace or goddess who, in bygone days, did not disdain to nip down to the stable with an armful of hay, and has been glimpsed by shepherds, bent into a north-easter, heading for a snowdrift that had overwhelmed some ewes?

It's no good asking the computer. We do not know how to programme the question. All we know is that something has got left out of the equation; we even wonder whether it is a good idea to live by an equation at all. (Like the architect of Ulm cathedral who, discovering that he had paid more heed to Euclid's theorems than to divine inspiration, committed suicide.) Better a dinner of herbs where love is, than the stalled ox and hatred therewith. Love might not show up on the gas chromatograph, and would cause a terrible to-do among the electronic valves. Better cut it right out, as it has been cut out of the feed-lot, the battery cage and the latest controlled-environment house. A maverick, that is what it is—unbranded. Uncontrolled.

Bibliography

As this is not a scientific treatise, I have not attempted to produce a complete bibliography or annotated text. The following notes, however, give the sources of some of the material I have drawn upon, where these are not mentioned in the text. But I have also drawn heavily on letters and conversations with various experts and authorities, and in these instances no published references are available.

General

Animal Dispersal in Relation to Social Behaviour. V. C. Wynne-Edwards. Oliver and Boyd, 1962.

The Behaviour of Domestic Animals. E. S. F. Hafez. Ballière, Tyndall & Cox, 1962.

Silent Spring. Rachel Carson. Hamish Hamilton, 1963.

Animal Machines. Ruth Harrison. Vincent Stewart, Stuart, 1964.

Human Ecology. Sir George Stapledon. Faber & Faber, 1964.

The Quiet Crisis. Stewart L. Udall. Holt, Rinehart & Winston, 1963.

Chapter 1

Food & Agriculture Organisation of the United Nations: *Third World Food Survey*, Basic Study No. 11.

F. A. O. Report: *The State of Food and Agriculture*, 1964.

A Handbook on Developing Countries: Commonwealth & International Library, 1964.

Fertility and Survival. Alfred Sauvy. Chatto & Windus, 1961.

"Food and Agriculture in 1984." B. R. Sen (Director-General, F.A.O.). *New Scientist*, January 30, 1964.

U.N. Demographic Yearbook, 1963.

U.N. Monthly Bulletin of Statistics, November 1964.

"Human Survival: The Essential Conditions." N. W. Pirie, *Discovery*, October 1963.

Chapter 2

Egg Quality. B.O.C.M. publication, 1963.

"Poultry Husbandry and the Peck Order." G. McBride, University of Queensland. *British Poultry Science*, 1, 65-68, 1960.

"Social Behaviour Studies on Domestic Animals. Hens in Laying Cages." J. W. James & F. Foenander, University of Queensland. *Australian Journal of Agricultural Research*, 12, 1961.

"Influence of Diet and Husbandry on the Nutritional Value of the Hen's Egg." J. B. M. Coppock & N. W. R. Daniels. *J. of Science of Food & Agriculture*, No. 9, 1962.

"A Comparison of Free Range and Battery Hens' Eggs etc." Coppock, Daniels, Gresham & Howard. *J. of Atherosclerosis Research*, 2, 1962.

"An Experiment with a Constant Environment for the Domestic Fowl." Alan W. G. Greenwood, A.R.C. Poultry Research Centre, Edinburgh. *Animal Production*, Vol. 4, Part 1, 1962.

"Mode of Life of the Domestic Fowl." E. Baeumer. *Zeitschrift für Tierpsychologie*, 19, 394. 1962.

Houghton Poultry Research Station, Houghton, Huntingdon. Annual Reports, 1958-63.

Chapter 3

"Broiler Industry: Looking into the Future." R. Coles, Chief Poultry Officer, N.A.A.S. *N.A.A.S. Quarterly Review*, 60, 1963.

Poultry, a Modern Agribusiness. Geoffrey Sykes. Crosby, Lockwood & Son, 1963.

Chapter 4

"Problems Arising from the Use of Feedingstuff Additives." R. Scarisbrook. *J. of Farmers' Club*, 1, 1960.

Antibiotics in Agriculture. Proceedings of University of Nottingham 9th Easter School in Agricultural Science, 1962. Ed. M. Woodbine.

Food and Cosmetics Toxicology, 2, 1964, 1 April 1964. British Industrial Biological Association. Pergamon Press.

Nutritional Research Unit, Huntingdon Research Centre. Report, 1952-61.

"The Effects of Incorporating Sulphadimidine-Pteridine Mixtures in the Diet of Young Chicks." Allan & Street. *British Vet. J.*, 118, 1962.

"The Fluoroacetamide Story." *Health & Life*, April 1964.

Mother Earth. Journal of the Soil Association. "Pesticides and The Smarden Affair," F. T. D. Good; "The Deterioration of Health," Dr Aubrey T. Westlake. April and July 1964.

Chapter 5

"Pathogen-free Pigs for Research and the Practical Control of Pig Diseases." A. O. Betts. *Veterinary Record*, Dec. 9, Vol. 73, No. 49, 1961.

"Environmental Studies in Pig Housing." W. A. M. Gordon, Belfast. I—V. *British Veterinary Journal*, May 1962; June 1962; May 1963; June 1963; July 1963 (119).

"Disease-free Pigs by the Caesarian Operation." N. S. Barron. *Animal Health*, Vol. I, No. 2, 1963.

"Pigs and Poisons." *Farm and Country*, May 1964.

"SFP Pigs." *Pig Farming*, January and February 1963.

Chapter 6

Crossbreeding and Hill Sheep. J. L. Read. Report of the Animal Breeding Research Organisation, Edinburgh, 1964.

"Hill Sheep and their Pasture." R. F. Hunter, *J. of Ecology*, 50, November 1962.

"Effect of Method of Rearing on the Social Behaviour of Scottish Blackface Hoggets." Hunter & Davies. *Animal Production*, Vol. 5, Part 2, June 1963.

"Behaviour of Individual and Related and Groups of South Country Cheviot Hill Sheep." Hunter & Milner. *Animal Behaviour*, II, October 1963.

"Home Range Behaviour in Hill Sheep." R. F. Hunter, paper read to British Ecological Society, Bangor, 1962.

Animal Breeding Research Organisation, Edinburgh. Annual Reports, 1958-1962.

Chapter 7

Producing Quality Veal from British Calves. Tj. Bakker, Christopher Hill Ltd., Poole, Dorset.

"Marketing Today: Veal and Eggs." Mansfield & Eastwood. *Agriculture*, Vol. 71, No. 4, April 1964.

"Intensive Calf Rearing for Veal Production." Report on a Visit to Holland by the President of the British Veterinary Association. *Veterinary Record*, August 27, 1960.

Chapter 8

"Beef Production." Paper by Dr Tj. Bakker read to National Farmers' Union, February 25th, 1964.

"Barley-Beef Production." T. R. Preston, Rowett Research Institute, Bucksburn, Aberdeen. Paper read to 81st Annual Congress of British Veterinary Assn., Llandudno, 1963.

"Intensive Beef Production." Preston & others. *Animal Production*, Vol. 5, Parts 1 and 3, February and October 1963.

"Feeding Systems in the Beef Industry." D. G. Dempster. *The Advancement of Science*, May 1964. Symposium at Aberdeen Meeting of the British Association.

Sealed Grain Storage and the Livestock Engineering Revolution. I. J. C. Friend. Lawrence Engineering Co. Ltd., Tipton, Staffs.

"Sealed Grain Storage." I. J. C. Friend. *Farm Mechanisation*, October 1963.

"Long Continued Oestrogen Administration to Fowls." Alan Greenwood, A.R.C. Poultry Research Station, Edinburgh. *Animal Production*, Vol. 4, Part 2, June 1962.

"Antibiotics for the Young Ruminant." T. R. Preston, *Antibiotics in Agriculture*, Ed. M. Woodbine, Butterworth 1962.

Rowett Research Institute, Aberdeen. *Intensive Production of Meat and Milk*. May 1965.

"Dairy Herds and Beef Supplies." Joseph Edwards, Milk Marketing Board. Paper read before Symposium on Animal Production, Rome, August 1963.

Health and Hormones. A. Stuart Mason. Penguin Books, 1963.

"The Use of Serum Gonadotrophin in the Induction of Twin-Pregnancy in the Cow." Gordon, Williams and Edwards. *J. Agric. Science*, 59, 142, 1962.

Chapter 9

The Listener. November 5 and 12, 1964.

"Social Behaviour in Domestic Animals: Effect of Peck Order." G. McBride, *Animal Production*, February 1964.

"The Problem of Live-Trapping and Population Estimates for the Wood Mouse." M. T. Tranton. *J. of Animal Ecology*, 34, 1-22, February 1965.

The Communal Organisation of Solitary Mammals. Paul Leyhausen, Max-Planck Institut fur Verhaltensphysiologie, Wuppertal-Elberfeld.

"Smaller Cats in the Zoo." P. Leyhausen, *Int. Zoo Year Book*, Vol. 3, 1961.

"Physiological Effects of Social Stress in Wild Rats." S. A. Barnett, University of Glasgow. *J. of Psychosomatic Res.*, Vol. 3, No. 1, 1958.

Chapter 10

Domestic Food Consumption and Expenditure, 1961. Annual Report of Food Survey Committee. H.M.S.O., 1963.

The Industrial Production of Protein from Vegetable Material. British Glues & Chemicals Ltd., 1959.

"Patterns and Trends in Food Consumption." John Yudkin. *Diogenes Progress*, February 1964.

"Nutrition and Palatability." John Yudkin. *Lancet*, June 22, 1963.

"Edible Protein from Leaves." N. W. Pirie. *British Vegetarian*, November-December 1959.

"Progress in Biological Engineering." N. W. Pirie. *Economic Botany*, October-December 1961.

"The Need for New Thinking on Food Production." N. W. Pirie. *J. Agric. Soc.*, Univ. Coll. of Wales, 44, 1963.

"Non-Conventional Protein Sources." N. W. Pirie. *Biochemistry and Biophysics in Food Research*. Butterworth, 1963.

"Changing Patterns of Food Consumption." B. T. Ramm. *J. Assn. of Agric.*, July 1964.

Investment in Food. Unilever, 1964.

Some Notes on Nutrition Policy in the U.K. M.A.F.F., 1962.

Manual of Nutrition. M.A.F.F. H.M.S.O., 1961.

Taste and Flavour. Report of Agr. Res. Council 1959-60. H.M.S.O., 1961.

"The Composition of Broilers and Free Range Chickens." D. F. Hollingsworth. Paper read to the Nutrition Society.

"Recent Advances in Food Science—3. Biochemistry and Biophysics in Food Research." Leitch & Rhodes. Advance Study Course, Cambridge, September 1962.

Chapter 11

"Toxic Effects of Pest-Control Agents." A. G. MacGregor. *Advancement of Science*, May 1964.

"Rachel Carson Replies to her Critics." *Health*, Vol. 8, 92, April 1964.

Jealott's Hill Research Station. *Field Guide to Experiments*, 1964.
—— Research Establishments in Europe: 34. D. J. Halliday, 1964.

Modifications in Agricultural Practices by the Use of Chemicals. S. H. Crowdy, Jealott's Hill Research Station, Bracknell.

Agricultural Chemicals. S. Laverton. Assn. of British Manufacturers of Agric. Chemicals, May 1962.

Poisonous Chemicals on the Farm. Notes for the Guidance of Medical Practitioners. Ministry of Health.

Agricultural Chemicals Approval Scheme. List of Approved Products, 1964. M.A.F.F.

"Some Occupational Disease Hazards: Chemical Pesticides." E. F. Edson. *Occupational Health*, Vol. XV, No. 2, 1963.

"Agricultural Pesticides." E. F. Edson. *British Medical Journal* Vol. 1, 841.

Weed Research Organisation, Agr. Res. Council, Kidlington: Annual Reports.

Toxic Chemicals in Agriculture. Report of the Working Party (Zuckerman Report). H.M.S.O., 1951.

Toxic Chemicals in Agriculture. Report of the Working Party (Zuckerman Report II). H.M.S.O., 1953.

Toxic Chemicals in Agriculture and Food Storage. Report of Research Study Group (Sanders Committee). 1961.

Report of the Research Committee on Toxic Chemicals (Frazer Committee). Agric. Res. Council, 1964.

Review of the Persistent Organochlorine Pesticides. Report by Advisory Committee on Poisonous Substances Used in Agriculture and Food Storage (Cook Committee). H.M.S.O., 1964.

"Crop Protection and World Food." K. Hassall, Reading. *Worcs. Agric. J.*, Vol. 29, No. 2, 1963-64.

Pesticides: Use and Misuse. K. Hassall, University of Reading.

Report of President Kennedy's Science Advisory Committee, May 1963.

Chapter 12

Injury to Glasshouse Crops by TBA Residues in Straw Manure. M.A.F.F., May, 1964.

"The Uptake of Hexoestrol by the Roots of Plants and Its Retention." Glacock & Hewitt. *Annals of Applied Biology*, 52, 1963.

Mother Earth. Journal of the Soil Association, published quarterly, 1960-65.

The Haughley Experiment. 1938-62. Summary of the first 25

years. The Soil Association, New Bells Farm, Haughley, Stowmarket, Suffolk.

The Haughley Experiment. Annual Reports, 1960-64. Soil Association.

Annual Reports of the Welsh Plant Breeding Station, Aberystwyth (University College of Wales). 1958-1963.

Eating, Drinking and Smoking. Twentieth Century Fund Survey, 1964. (U.S.)

Chapter 13

Toxic Chemicals in Agriculture: Risks to Wildlife. Report of Working Party, H.M.S.O., 1955.

"The Past and Present Status of the Buzzard in the British Isles." N. W. Moore. *British Birds*, Vol. 1, May 1957.

"Man, Pesticides and the Conservation of Wildlife." N. W. Moore. The British Social Biology Council, 69. *Biology and Human Affairs*, Vol. 29, No. 2, 1964.

"Organic Chlorine Insecticide Residues in Wild Birds." Moore & Walker. *Nature*, Vol. 201, No. 4924, March 14, 1964.

"Toxic Chemicals and Birds: the Ecological Background." N. W. Moore. *British Birds*, Vol. 55, 1962.

Annual Reports of Nature Conservancy Research Station, Monks' Wood, Huntingdonshire.

"Hedges." J. M. Way and B. N. K. Davis. *Agriculture*, December 1963.

"The Heaths of Dorset and their Conservation." N. W. Moore. *J. of Ecology*, 50, July 1962.

The Return of the Native. Thomas Hardy.

"The Foraging of Bumble Bees." A. D. Brian. *Bee World*, 35, 1954.

"Beekeeping and Agricultural Sprays." B. A. Cooper. *Yearbook of Lincolnshire Beekeepers' Association*, April 1951.

"Is There any Solution to the Spray-Poisoning Problem?" O. Hammer, *Bee World*, 34 (3), 1953.

"Lichens." F. N. Haynes. *Viewpoints in Biology*, Vol. III.

Spraying of Roadside Verges to Control Weed and Grass Growth. Experiments at Bibury, 1952-64. Baywood Chemicals Ltd., London.

Radiobiological Laboratories, Agricultural Research Council. Annual Reports, 1962 and 1963.

——Radioactivity in Milk: December 1961 and February 1964.

—— Interim Report on Radioactivity in Diet. May 1962.

"Observations on the Effect of Hexoestrol on Earthworms." F. Raw., Rothamsted Experimental Station. *J. of Agric. Science*, 55, 1, 1960.

Chapter 14

"Agriculture, Forestry and Fisheries." *Germany Reports*, Federal Republic of Germany, 1961.

The Agriculture of the Federal Republic of Germany. Federal Ministry of Food, Agriculture and Forestry, Bonn, 1963.

Trends in Agriculture. A. N. Duckham, University of Reading. E.D.A. Rural Electrification Conference, 1964.

Future Trends in Agriculture. Rolf Gardiner. Institute of Landscape Architects, May 1964.

Chapter 15

The Quantitative Society, or What are You to Do with Noodle? John Wilkinson. Centre for the Study of Democratic Institutions, Santa Barbara, Calif., 1964.

Inventing the Future. Dennis Gabor. Penguin Books, 1963.

Territory in Bird Life. Eliot Howard. John Murray, 1920.

KING ALFRED'S COLLEGE

LIBRARY